PERPLEXING
PUZZLES

CRYPTIC
CHALLENGES

REMARKABLE
RIDDLES

First published by Parragon in 2012

Parragon
Queen Street House
4 Queen Street
Bath BA1 1HE, UK
www.parragon.com

Produced by Tall Tree Books
Written by Rob Colson
Designed by Malcolm Parchment

Cover design by Michael Duffy

ISBN 978-1-4454-7582-0

Printed in Indonesia

Picture credits: (shutterstock unless stated)
2tr Steve Mann, 2tl donatas1205, 2-3 Atelier Sharaku, 4tl donatas1205, 4-5 chris scredon/istock, 5 Baloncici, 5 Zanico/dreamstime, 6-7 shalunts, 7b John Kershner, 7r shalunts, 8tl donatas1205, 8-9 Lebazele/istock, 9r Péter Gudella, 8-9 Eleonora Kolomiyets, 10 T.W., 10-11 Steve Mann, 11r Steve Mann, 12 Thorsten Schmitt, 12-13 stocknshares, 13br Steve Mann, 14bl Steve Mann, 14-15 Steve Mann, 15r Anna Jurkovska, 18b PILart, 18-19 titelio, 19r Steve Mann, 19c Mike Bentley/istock, 21l-r marekuliasz, 23t Yurchyks, 24 markrhiggins, 25r Sbelov, 26 donatas1205, 27r fuyu liu, 30-31 Tarek El Sombati/istock, 31b Sergio Schnitzler, 33c Stephen Morris, 32-33 Novitech, 34 granata1111, 34 William Bacon, 35tr fuyu liu, 34-35 fuyu liu, 35b Valentin Agapov, 38l markrhiggins, 38b dreamstime, 38-39 Chereshnya/dreamstime, 39 Tischenko Irina/dreamstime, 40 IDAL/dreamstime, 42 Stephen Coburn, 42-43 donatas1205, 43b jörg röse -oberreich, 44 tanewpix, 45 Feliks Kogan, 46 loriklaszlo, 46b colillusion bricks, 46-47 Fotana, 50 Selahattin Bayram/istock, 52tl Crom, 52 Steve Mann, 54-55 Marafona, 56tl Atelier Sharaku, 57br Eleonora Kolomiyets, 58b Helen Cingisiz, 60-61 Lebazele/istock, 61tr androfroll, 64 shutterstock, 65tl BW Folsom, 66bl Worldpics, 66b Orla, 69 Margo Harrison, 70cl SVLuma, 71tr Ron Peigl/istockphoto, 74-75c Arie v.d. Wolde, 74-75b Eleonora Kolomiyets, 75br Steve Mann, 76tl tanewpix, 76-77 Péter Gudella, 76bc Mike Bentley/istock, 77c Marilyn Volan, 78-79t stocknshares/istock, 79tr Stephen Coburn, 80tl holbox, 82r Kesamasek, 86-87 Lebazele, 88b Guy Shapira, 88-89 chris scredon/istock, 93bc Nicemonkey, 94bl Alexander Ishchenko, 95c khz, 96l-r RoxyFer, 98-99tc Steve Mann, 100b Evgeny Karandaev, 100l Gordon Galbraith, 100-101tc titelio, 101r Worldpics, 101b Jasenka, 104l Krasowit, 104c oriontrail, 105rc John Kershner, 105rb markrhiggins, 108-109 Brad Remy, 110 Ivan Bondarenko, 111 bioraven, 118 Michael Klenetsky, 122 Nejron Photo, 136 Baloncici, 140 Jim Barber, 142 nando viciano, 144 Transition, 146 Gordana Sermek, 158 Sergik, 161 Benjamin Haas, 163 Africa Studio

Remember these from school?

For some of the puzzles, you will need a few simple mathematical formulae to hand.

Pythagoras' theorem for right-angled triangles is the most important one:

The square of the hypotenuse is equal to the sum of the squares of the other two sides.

To work out the area of a circle you need the number π (pi), which equals about 3.14.

The area of a circle equals πr^2, where r is the radius. The circumference of a circle equals $2\pi r$.

At one point, you'll need to think about similar triangles – remember that if the internal angles of two triangles are the same, the proportions between the lengths of their sides will also be the same.

INTRODUCTION

Beware! Thinking about these 300 brain-teasers may well make your head hurt. Like a devious magician, the puzzles will try to fool you by misdirection, using subtle cues to lead your thinking in completely the wrong direction. All may not be as it first appears.

The puzzles in this book will test your ability with numbers, logical reasoning, spatial awareness and powers of imagination. There are paradoxes dating back to the Ancient Greeks, classic conundrums from nineteenth-century puzzlers, such as Sam Loyd and Henry Dudeney, plus modern takes on old themes and brand new teasers. Keep a box of matches handy. Dotted through the book are some fiendish problems where you're going to need them.

Don't worry if you cannot see how to do all of them. Many of these puzzles are easier than they look, but there are also some really tough ones, which will test even the most experienced puzzler. All the answers are in the back, but try not to peek until you've had a good think. The pleasure of knowing the answer is made all the sweeter by having discovered it for yourself.

Dr and Mrs Maxwell's son was born on Monday, 29 February 1892. How old was he the next time his birthday fell on a Monday?

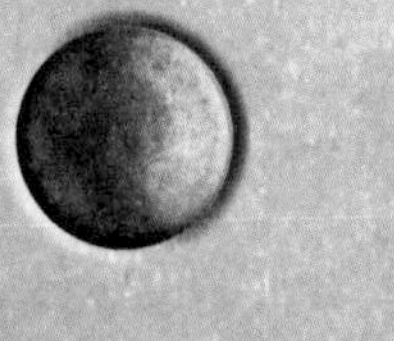

Solution on p. 175

Can you join the dots to make the shape of an envelope without lifting the pen from the paper?

Solution on p. 175

3 SECRET MESSAGE

Connie needs to send a secret message in a box to Neville at the other side of town. They both have a padlock, but for security reasons, they only have keys for their own padlocks. How can Connie send the message to Neville in such a way that Neville can open the box, but any nosy messenger cannot look inside?

Solution on p. 175

4 Palindromes

Phileas Fogg notices that he has travelled 15951 kilometres since leaving London on his round-the-world journey. He sees that this number is a palindrome (reads the same from left to right as from right to left), and decides to keep an eye out for the next one. Two days later, he notices that his distance is again a palindrome. How far did he travel in those two days?

Solution on p. 175

5 TWO SQUARES

Move two matches to make two squares.

Solution on p. 175

6 THE DAY TODAY?

When the day after tomorrow is yesterday, today will be as far from Tuesday as that day was which was today when the day before yesterday was tomorrow.

What day is it?

Solution on p. 175

7 NEXT NUMBER

What is the next number in the sequence:

1, 3, 4, 7, 11, 18, ??

Solution on p. 176

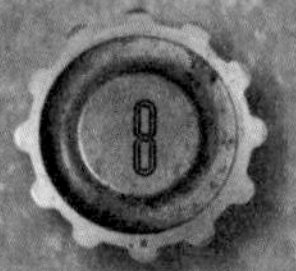

8 Three squares

Make three squares by
moving four matches.

Solution on p. 176

9 BOXED UP

Adam the sculptor has made a giant cube out of wooden boards measuring 2 metres by 2 metres. Adam can see all six sides of his cube from where he is standing. Where is Adam standing?

Solution on p. 176

10 Circular reasoning

How would you make a perfect circle using only these eight straight lines?

Solution on p. 176

11 Rising tide

A boat floats in the harbour at low tide. A ladder is fixed to the side of the boat, and five rungs of the ladder are showing above the waterline. If the rungs are 20 cm apart and the sea level rises at a rate of 35 cm per hour, how many rungs will be showing above water after two and a half hours?

Solution on p. 176

12 Diophantus' Epitaph

The gravestone of the Greek mathematician Diophantus was said to have contained this riddle:

'God gave him his boyhood one-sixth of his life;
One-twelfth more as youth while whiskers grew rife;
And then yet one-seventh ere marriage begun.
In five years there came a bouncing new son.
Alas, the dear child of master and sage
After attaining half the measure of his
father's life, chill fate took him.
After consoling his fate by the science of numbers
for four years, he reached the end of his life.'

Can you work out how old Diophantus was when he died?

Solution on p. 176

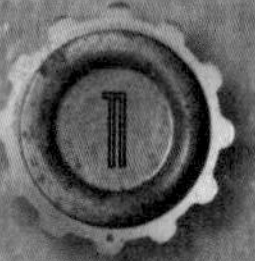

13 TRAIN DELAYS

Brunel's new train service from London to Oxford is 100 kilometres long. He advertises that the journey will be completed in 2 hours, making an average speed of 50 km/h. If the train completes the first 50 kilometres at 25 km/h, how fast will it have to go for the rest of the journey to make its average up to the required 50 km/h?

Solution on p. 177

14 Does this add up?

Replace the letters with numerals (0–9) to make this equation work (each letter represents a different numeral):

SEVEN + SEVEN + SIX = TWENTY

Solution on p. 177

15 String trio

Three friends, James, Elizabeth and Hannah, play in a chamber music group. Two out of the three play the violin, two play the viola and two play the cello. The one who doesn't play the violin doesn't play the viola either. The one who doesn't play the viola doesn't play the cello.

Which instruments do they all play if James doesn't play the violin?

Solution on p. 177

16 Classroom conundrum

Mrs Rogers' primary school class has just seven students this year. How can she arrange their desks so that there are six rows with three students sat along each row?

Solution on p. 177

17 Equal shares

Mrs Brown is late getting to the shops. She buys the last five apples in the greengrocer, but she has six children, herself and a husband to feed. How does she share the fruit equally between all the family members?

Solution on p. 177

18 SUMMING UP

Move one match to make the sum correct.

Solution on p. 177

19 MATCHING SOCKS

Bradley is a very untidy boy. In his sock drawer, his socks are all mixed together. There are 14 red socks, 10 purple socks and 6 white socks. There has been a power cut and it is completely dark in his bedroom. What is the minimum number of socks that Bradley should take out of his drawer to be sure that he has at least two the same colour?

Solution on p. 178

20 A LONG MULTIPLICATION

What is the value of the following product:

$$(x - a)\,(x - b)\,(x - c)\,\ldots\,(x - y)\,(x - z)$$

There are 26 parentheses, and the variables *a–z* can be any number.

Solution on p. 178

21 A snail's pace

A snail starts to climb a wall one morning. The wall is 10 metres high. The snail makes good progress during the day, climbing at a rate of 3 metres a day. However, it slips back 2 metres every night. How many days does the snail take to reach the top of the wall?

Solution on p. 178

22 COUNT THE RECTANGLES

Professor Cordon is staring at his kitchen floor. How many different rectangles can he make out of the eight tiles?

Solution on p. 178

23 DRIP DROP

How many drops of wine can be put into an empty wine glass?

Solution on p. 178

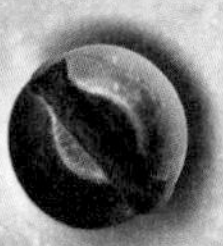

24 TRIANGULATION

Can you help Clive the plumber? He needs to join together these six pipes to make three equilateral triangles.

Solution on p. 178

25 CHESS MATES

In the monthly tournament at the Checkmates Chess Club, the number of competitors varies month by month, but the principle is always the same: a direct knockout, with the loser of each game leaving the tournament. In the event of a draw, the player with the black pieces wins. Depending on the numbers, some competitors may be given byes through the early rounds.

There are 55 competitors in March's competition. How many individual games are there in the whole tournament?

Solution on p. 179

26 Archer's score

Lily has set up an archery board in the garden. How can she score exactly 100 firing at a board with the following scores? (She may use as many arrows as she likes.)

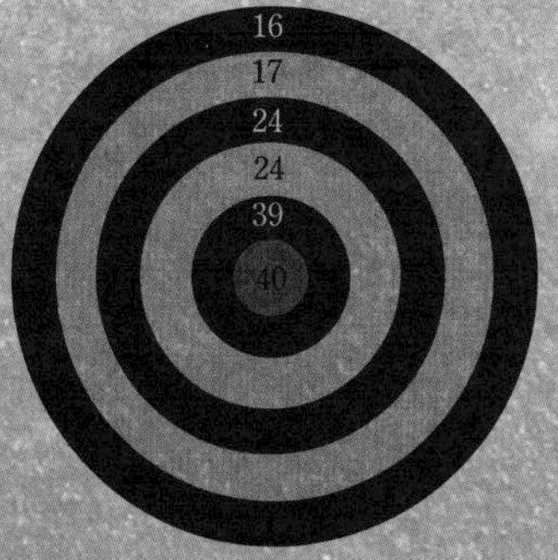

Solution on p. 179

27 The Monty Hall problem

This famous puzzle stumped even mathematics professors. Can you get it right?

A game show contestant stands on stage in front of three closed doors, numbered 1, 2 and 3. The host tells her that behind two of the doors is a goat, but behind one of them is a brand new car. The contestant is asked to choose a door, and goes for door number 1. The host opens door number 3 to reveal that there is a goat standing behind it munching on some grass. He now gives the contestant a choice: she can stick with door number 1 or she can change to door number 2.

What should the contestant do to give her the best chance of winning the car?

Solution on p. 179

28 PAY RISE, PAY CUT

Stephen earned £1,224.45 per year two years ago.
His salary increased by ¼ last year, then fell by ⅕ this year.

How much does he earn now?

Solution on p. 179

29 *Equal Areas*

These matches cover an area of 3 square matches. Can you move two matches and add two more, but keep the area they cover the same?

Solution on p. 179

DO RE MI

Replace the letters with numerals (0–9) to make these equations work (each letter represents a different numeral):

RE + MI = FA

DO + SI = MI

LA + SI = SOL

Solution on p. 179

SEPARATE SAMPLES

Dr Mulligan needs to keep his samples separated in their tray to prevent contamination. He can use two square dividers, which may be any size. How should he place the dividers?

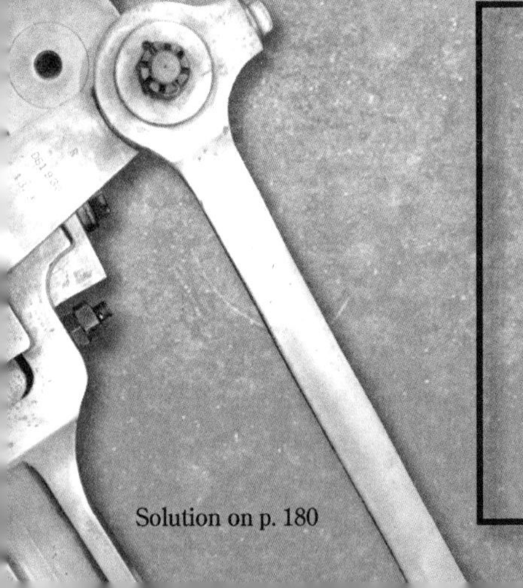
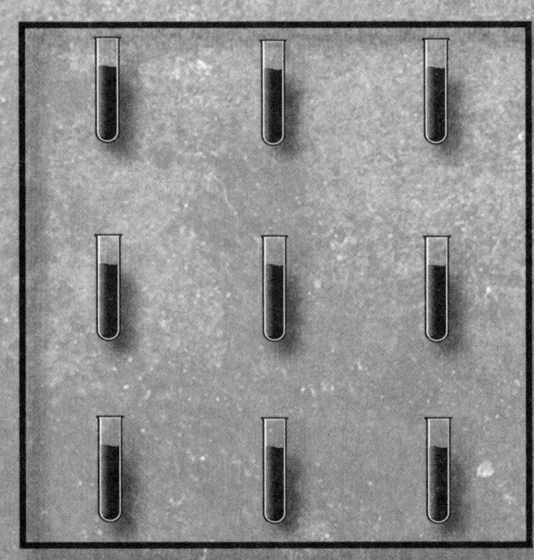

Solution on p. 180

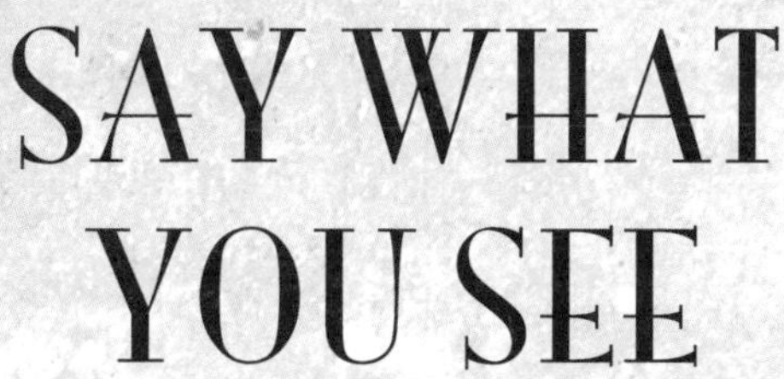

32 SAY WHAT YOU SEE

What is the next term in the series:

1
11
21
1211
111221
312211

Solution on p. 180

33 PICK UP STICKS

Professor Bell can only take one of his assistants Alexander and Graham to the science conference. To settle the matter, he proposes a game, and lays 21 sticks on the table. Taking turns, Alexander and Graham may pick up one, two or three sticks. Whoever picks up the final stick must stay at home and mind the laboratory.

They toss a coin to see who goes first, and Graham is first to pick. Alexander smiles, as he knows he is going to the conference. How does Alexander make sure he wins?

Solution on p. 180

34 Matching up

Move two matches to make this equation work.

Solution on p. 180

35 TOSS A COIN

Robin cannot decide whether to go to the pub or to stay in with his girlfriend. He decides to toss a coin to make his decision for him. He wants it to be equally likely that he will go to the pub as stay in. However, he knows the only coin he has is biased but doesn't know what the bias is. How can he use the biased coin to make his decision for him?

Solution on p. 180

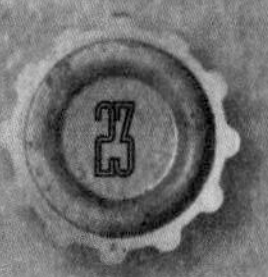

36 RUNNING DOG

Michael, Amanda and their dog Spike set out together for a walk. Michael walks at 6 km/h, while Amanda lags behind, doing 5 km/h. Spike, full of energy, runs back and forth between the two of them for the whole time at a speed of 12 km/h. They walk for an hour like this. How far does Spike run in this time?

Solution on p. 181

37 MISSING NUMBER

What is the next number in the following sequence:

7, 10, 8, 11, 9, 12, ??

Solution on p. 181

38 HOW LONG?

Which of the two horizontal lines is the longer?

Solution on p. 181

39 *Sunbathing sea lions*

Some sea lions are lying in the sun on two rocks in the harbour. The sea lions on the larger rock shout over to the sea lions on the smaller rock: 'If one of you comes over here, there will be twice as many sea lions in our group as in yours.' The sea lions on the smaller rock reply: 'Well, if one of you comes over here, our numbers will be equal.'

How many sea lions are there on each rock?

Solution on p. 181

40 LAWN MOWERS

Between them it takes gardening duo Geoffrey and Lewis eight days to mow all the lawns on their rounds, both working as fast as they can. On his own, Geoffrey can mow the lawns in 12 days. How many days would it take Lewis to mow the lawns on his own?

Solution on p. 181

41 Two Triangles

Move two matches to make two triangles.

Solution on p. 181

42 EQUAL SHARES

Farmer Barnett wants to be scrupulously fair to his four sons when he retires. Can you divide his land into four parts so that each part is the same size and shape, and has the same number of fields and woodland on it?

Solution on p. 181

43 Jealous guys

Three men and their fiancées need to cross a river by boat. Their boat only takes two people at a time, but the men are very protective, and agree to the following rule (much to the bemusement of their fiancées, it has to be said!): there must never be more men than women on either riverbank at any time, and the boat needs at least one person to row it.

How can our jealous guys achieve their aim?

Solution on p. 182

44 GWENDOLINE'S GRANNY

Gwendoline tells her friends that her grandmother is only one year older than her mother.

How can that be?

Solution on p. 182

45 SHADOWY SECRET

Which square is lighter, A or B?

Solution on p. 182

46 GEAR POWER

Stephenson is playing around with gear ratios for his new locomotive. He connects up five gears in a row, the first connected to the second, the second to the third and so on.

The second and fourth gears are twice the size of the first gear, the third gear is half the size of the first gear, while the fifth gear is the same size as the first gear. Stephenson gives the first gear one complete revolution.

How many times does the fifth gear turn?

Solution on p. 182

47 Gear Power II

If Stephenson turns the first gear in the above set of gears in a clockwise direction, what direction will the fourth gear turn in?

Solution on p. 182

48 WHO'S WHO?

Three identical triplets, Anne, Beatrix and Caroline, are visiting David's house for tea. They are sat in a line on the sofa, and David wants to work out which sister is which.

He knows that Anne always tells the truth, that Beatrix always lies, and that Caroline sometimes lies and sometimes tells the truth.

David asks the following questions:

He asks the sister on the left, 'Who is sat in the middle?'
She replies, 'That's Anne.'

He asks the sister in the middle, 'What is your name?'
She replies, 'I'm Caroline.'

He asks the sister on the right, 'Who is sat in the middle?'
She replies, 'That's Beatrix.'

David smiles. He now knows who is who.
How?

Solution on p. 182

49 CORRECT THE SUM

Move two matches to make this sum correct.

Solution on p. 183

50 A KNOTTY PROBLEM

Maskelyne the magician stands on stage holding a length of rope. He tells his audience that he can hold the rope with one end in each hand and tie a knot in it without letting go.

How does he do it?

Solution on p. 183

51 Bookworm

Dr Rutherford keeps his ten-volume *Encyclopedia Britannica* on its own shelf in the library, stored spine-out and in order from left to right. Each volume is 10 cm thick, including front and back covers that are each 1 cm thick.

Starting on page 1 of Volume 1, a bookworm eats its way in a straight line through the complete set, finishing on the last page of Volume 10.

What distance does the bookworm travel?

Solution on p. 183

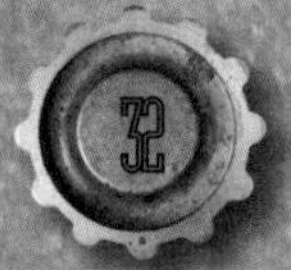

52 CHEATING THE CHEATER

Gordon is desperate to join the Magic Circle, but he knows that the devious Lord Sleight, its President, has it in for him. He is told to attend a meeting of the Inner Circle, where he will be asked to draw one of two marbles from a bag. One of the marbles will be white, the other black. If Gordon draws the white marble, he can join. If he draws the black marble, he will be excluded for life.

The night before the meeting, Gordon hears from his spies in the Circle that Lord Sleight is going to switch the marbles at the last minute and make them both black. What should Gordon do to make sure he can join?

Solution on p. 183

53

Replace the letters with numerals (0–9) to make this equation work (each letter represents a different numeral):

$$(AA)^B = ABBA$$

Solution on p. 183

54 SNOWED UNDER

It has been snowing heavily, and Mrs Thomas looks out into her back garden. She sees that there is three times as much snow in her garden than that of her neighbour, Mrs Brown. How can this be possible?

Solution on p. 183

SIGNALLING ERROR

55

Read this sign

PLEASE
LEAVE YOUR
HATS, COATS
AND BAGS AT
AT THE RECEPTION

Solution on p. 184

Now turn straight to the answer.

IRONMONGER

Mr Braithwaite is at the ironmonger's. He asks:

'What does 1 cost?'
'1 pound,' replies the ironmonger.
'And 10?'
'2 pounds.'
'What about 310?'
'That would be 3 pounds.'

What is Mr Braithwaite buying?

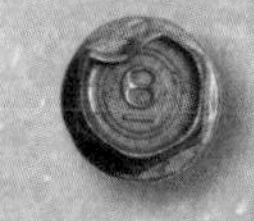

Solution on p. 184

57 Three squares

Move three matches to make three squares.

Solution on p. 184

58 Crescent moon

This crescent moon is formed of two circles. C is the centre of the larger circle. The width of the crescent between points B and D is 9 cm. Between points E and F, it is 5 cm. What are the diameters of the two circles?

Solution on p. 184

59 FOUR PINTS

Sat at a table in a pub are a father, a mother, a son, a daughter, a brother, a sister, two cousins, an uncle and an aunt. One of them goes to the bar to get a round of drinks in. She comes back with four pints of beer, but she has bought a drink for everyone. How?

Solution on p. 184

60 Pizza deal

Perfect Pizzas have a special offer this week. Buy any 20 cm Margherita pizza and you get a second half price. The 20 cm pizza costs £7, while the 30 cm pizza costs £10. Is their offer good value or are you better off buying one 30 cm pizza instead?

Solution on p. 184

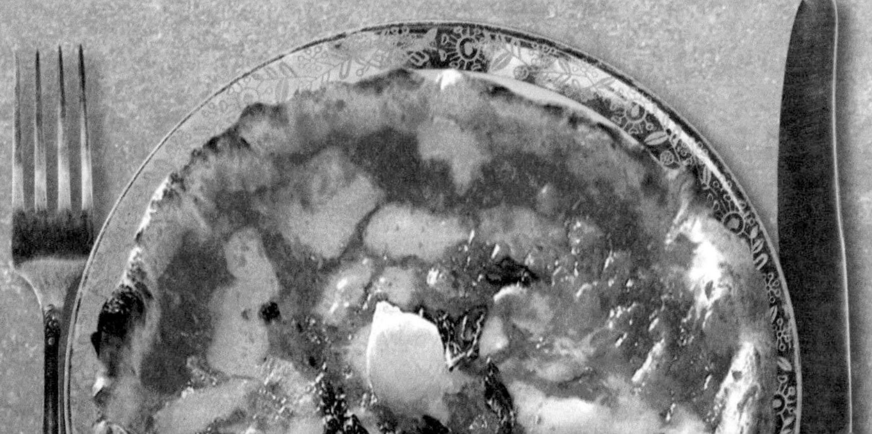

61 Four rectangles

Move two matches to make four identical rectangles.

Solution on p. 185

62 A perfect egg

Mrs Housman is very fussy about her eggs. She likes them hard-boiled for exactly 9 minutes. Her husband has two hourglasses, one measuring 7 minutes and the other 4 minutes. How can he cook the eggs to his wife's satisfaction using just these hourglasses?

Solution on p. 185

63 MUNCH, MUNCH

Can you slice this square into four identical shapes, each with one caterpillar in it, plus a leaf for the caterpillar to munch on?

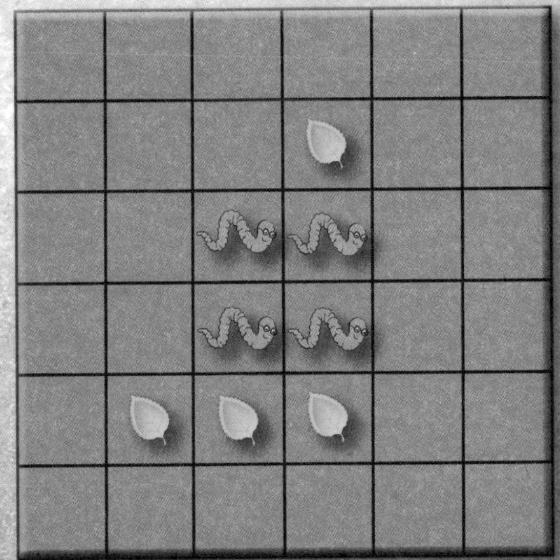

Solution on p. 185

64 Growth spurt

Mrs Morgan measures her son Malcolm's height with a mark on the wall. When Malcolm asks how tall he is, she replies, 'You're 60 centimetres plus half your height.'

How tall is Malcolm?

Solution on p. 185

65

A GRAINY PROBLEM

A poor farmer needs to go to the market to sell some grain and some lentils. He only has one sack to carry them in, but doesn't want to mix the grain with the lentils. He pours the grain in first, ties the middle of the sack, and fills the top half with the lentils. At the market, a brewer offers to buy the grain, but he has no use for the lentils. The brewer has his own sack to take the grain away in. The farmer wants to sell the brewer the grain, but needs to keep the lentils. They cannot cut either of the sacks, and they have to keep their own sacks. Pouring the produce anywhere on the ground would spoil it.

How does the farmer solve this conundrum?

Solution on p. 185

66 Fractions

65 per cent can be written as the fraction $\frac{13}{20}$ (with the lowest possible denominator). How would you write $58\frac{1}{3}$ per cent as a simplified fraction with the lowest possible denominator?

Solution on p. 185

67 TAKE AWAY A SQUARE

Move three matches to turn these five squares into four.

Solution on p. 186

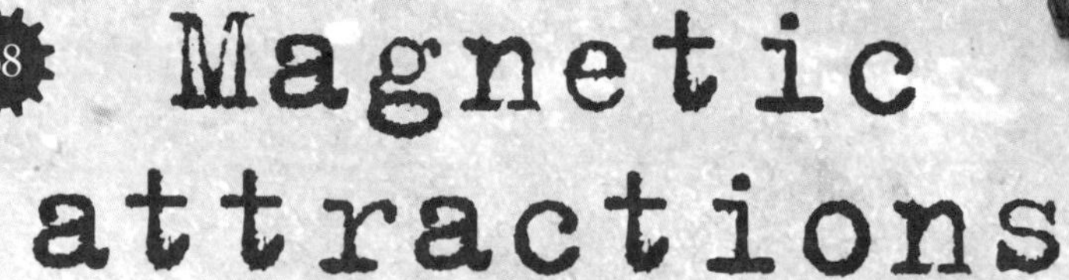

68 Magnetic attractions

Faraday is standing in a room wearing nothing but his pyjamas. The room is empty save for a wooden table with two iron rods placed on it. One of the rods is a magnet.

How does Faraday work out which iron rod is the magnet?

Solution on p. 186

69 A LONG SUM

What is the sum of the first 100 whole numbers? That is:

1 + 2 + 3 ... + 99 + 100

(Clue: you do not need to add them all up.)

Solution on p. 186

70 Crippen's cell

Dr Crippen the murderer has been locked in a round cell. He has had all his possessions taken from him, except his pocket compass. Starting from the window of the cell, which is not facing due south, Crippen takes three paces due north, where he reaches the wall of the cell. He then turns 90° and takes four paces due west before reaching the wall again.

How many paces is the diameter of Dr Crippen's cell?

Solution on p. 186

71 Eight triangles

Arrange these six matches to form eight equilateral triangles.

Solution on p. 186

72 A grave problem

Thomas the gravedigger sits back for a well-earned rest. He has just dug a grave 2.5 metres long, 0.7 metres wide and 2 metres deep.

Can you calculate how much earth there is in the grave?

Solution on p. 187

73 TURNING CARDS

Can you turn all four of these playing cards upside down by turning three at a time?

What is the minimum number of goes you can do it in?

Solution on p. 187

74 MISSING NUMBER

What is the missing number in this series?

??, 49, 2401, 5764801

Solution on p. 187

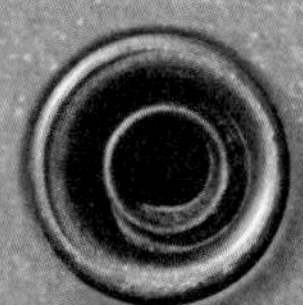

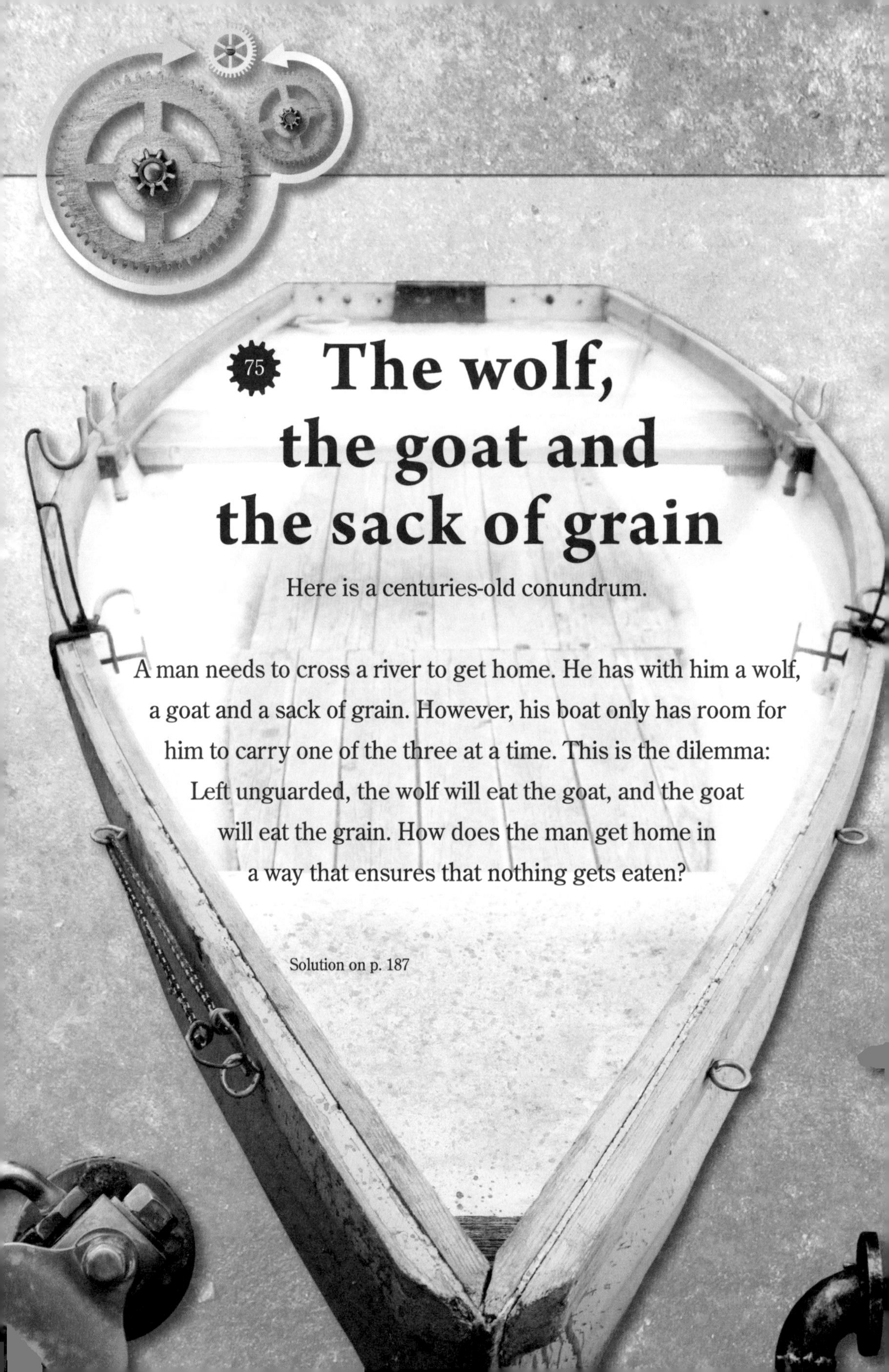

75 The wolf, the goat and the sack of grain

Here is a centuries-old conundrum.

A man needs to cross a river to get home. He has with him a wolf, a goat and a sack of grain. However, his boat only has room for him to carry one of the three at a time. This is the dilemma: Left unguarded, the wolf will eat the goat, and the goat will eat the grain. How does the man get home in a way that ensures that nothing gets eaten?

Solution on p. 187

76 FIVE SQUARES

Move two matches to make five squares all the same size.

Solution on p. 187

77 FIGURE OF EIGHT

Marie is numbering her laboratory log book by hand.
The book has 100 pages, so she numbers them from 1 to 100.

How many times will she write the figure 8?

Solution on p. 187

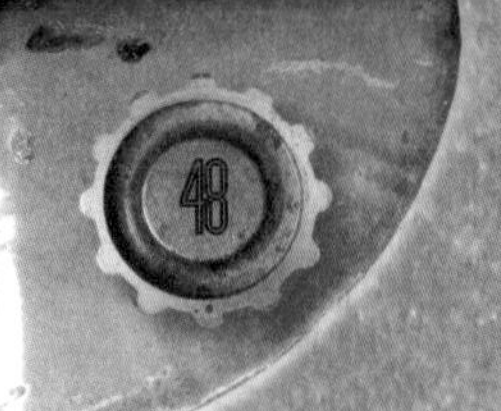

78 The mountaineer

Mummery the mountaineer sets out at 5 am to climb Ben Nevis. He reaches the summit at noon, and stays there for the rest of the day and night staring at the stars. The following morning, he starts his descent at 5 am and, retracing his steps, he arrives back in town at 10 am. Did Mummery find himself at any point along his route at the same place and the same time on both days?

Solution on p. 187

79 *Parallel thinking*

Are these lines parallel, or are they sloping towards each other?

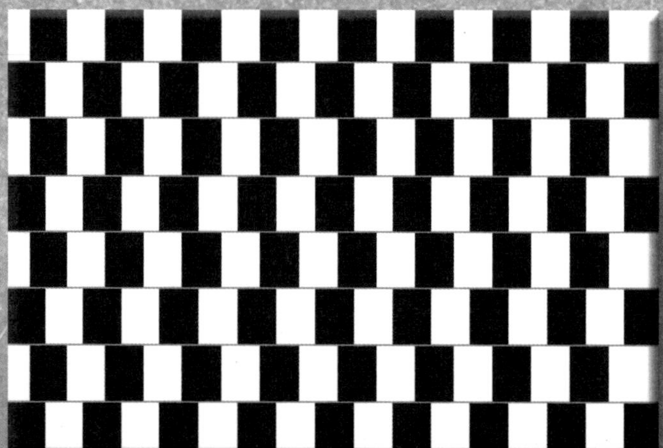

Solution on p. 188

80 NORTH FACING

The four sides of a house all face due north.
Where is the house?

Solution on p. 188

81 THE KANGAROO AND THE WALLABY

A kangaroo and a wallaby are set in a race against each other. From the starting line, they hop to a pole 100 metres away, then turn immediately and come back again. The kangaroo covers 3 metres with each hop, and the wallaby 2 metres. The wallaby makes three hops for every two hops of the kangaroo.

Which marsupial will win?

Solution on p. 188

82 THE CARPENTER'S PROBLEM

A carpenter wants to make a square tabletop from this piece of wood. The tabletop needs to be as large as possible and made from as few pieces as possible.
How many pieces will the carpenter need to cut the wood into?

Solution on p. 188

83 DOODLE'S A DODDLE

Bored in class, Joseph draws on his notebook. How many squares can you count in Joseph's geometric doodle?

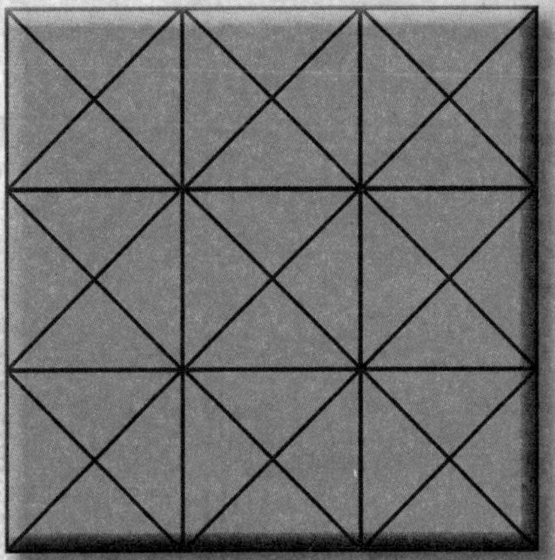

Solution on p. 188

84 Watch the cards

Geraldine lays down four cards in front of her, side by side. The cards are numbered 2 to 5. She wants to rearrange the cards so that they are in ascending order from her left to her right. John is sat opposite Geraldine and watches her take the card on John's left and move it to the other end. She then takes the third card from John's right and puts it to the end on the left from John's perspective.

What was the original order of the cards?

Solution on p. 188

85 FIVE MOVES

Move five matches to make five triangles.

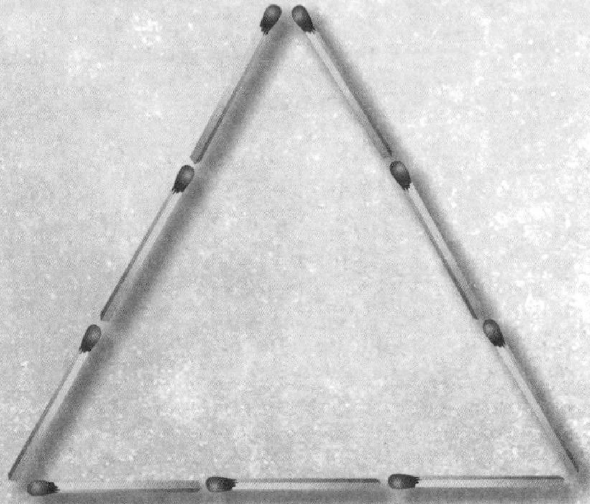

Solution on p. 189

86 Who's the grandad?

Harvey is the son of Mary. Mary is the sister of Martin. Patrick is the brother of Harvey. Theresa is the daughter of Martin. Martin is the son of Elijah.

Who is Patrick's grandfather?

Solution on p. 189

87 BLACK AND WHITE

In this grid there are white and black draughts pieces. The horizontal rows are labelled 1–4 and the vertical columns are labelled A–D. Each piece is the opposite colour on its reverse side, so turning it over changes its colour.

Choosing one row or column at a time and turning over all four pieces in that line in one go, what is the minimum number of goes you would need to turn all the draughts black?

Solution on p. 189

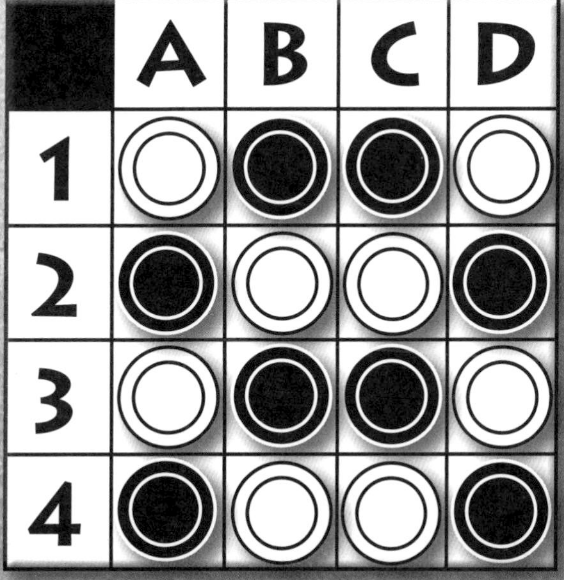

88 Think laterally

Move one match to make the scales balance.

(The answer is sneaky!)

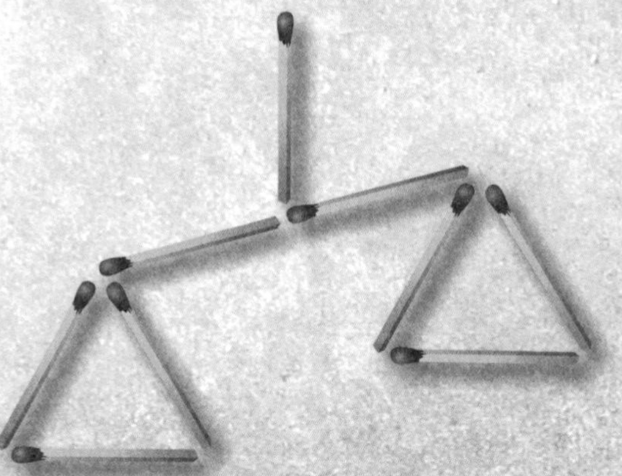

Solution on p. 189

89 WAR AND PEACE

How would you balance a copy of Tolstoy's epic novel, *War and Peace*, all 1,000 pages of it, on a single piece of paper?

Solution on p. 189

PICKY PROBLEM

Arrange 13 toothpicks to make the following incorrect equation:

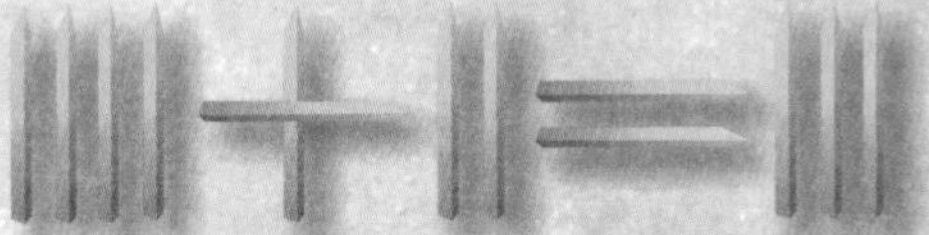

Now move one toothpick to make the equation correct. (You are not allowed to change the = sign!)

Solution on p. 189

Trouble at t'mill

Mrs Trubshaw is boasting again. Invited to dinner at the Braithwaites', she declares, 'One hundred and fifty people work at my husband's mill.' Mrs Braithwaite's troublesome daughter Rose begs to differ. 'I know there are not that many,' she says. Her son Reginald, ever the peacemaker, says, 'Well, I'm sure there is at least one worker at the mill.' All the while, Mr Trubshaw is squirming in his seat. He knows that only one of them is right.

How many workers are there at Mr Trubshaw's mill?

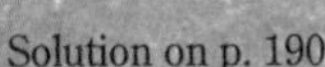
Solution on p. 190

Half a dozen

Here are 14 matches.

How would you take away seven to leave a dozen?

Solution on p. 190

Taking stock

Dr Watson is doing a stocktaking. At the start of the year, his bottle of rubbing alcohol was full and weighed 5 kg. Now it is half-full and weighs 3 kg.

How much does the empty bottle weigh?

Solution on p. 190

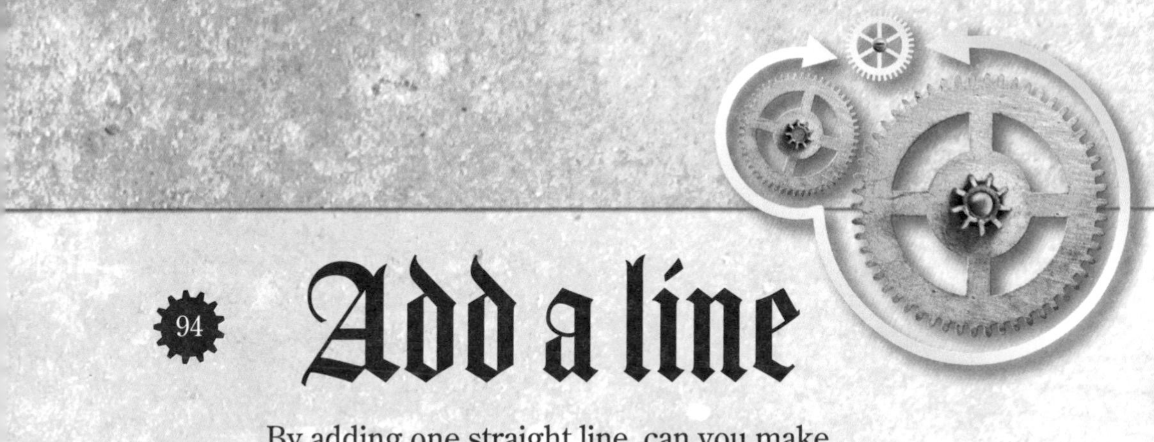

94 Add a line

By adding one straight line, can you make the following equation add up?

5+5+5=550

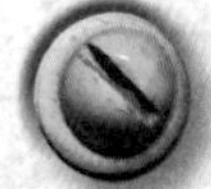

Solution on p. 190

95 Reckless driving

Daimler is out driving his new car, and the car's lights have stopped working again. Nonetheless, he drives on at high speed. There are no streetlights to show him the way and there is no moonlight. A woman dressed from head to toe in black steps out into the road. Despite all this, Daimler sees the woman, brakes and manages to stop the car before he runs her over.

How was this possible?

Solution on p. 190

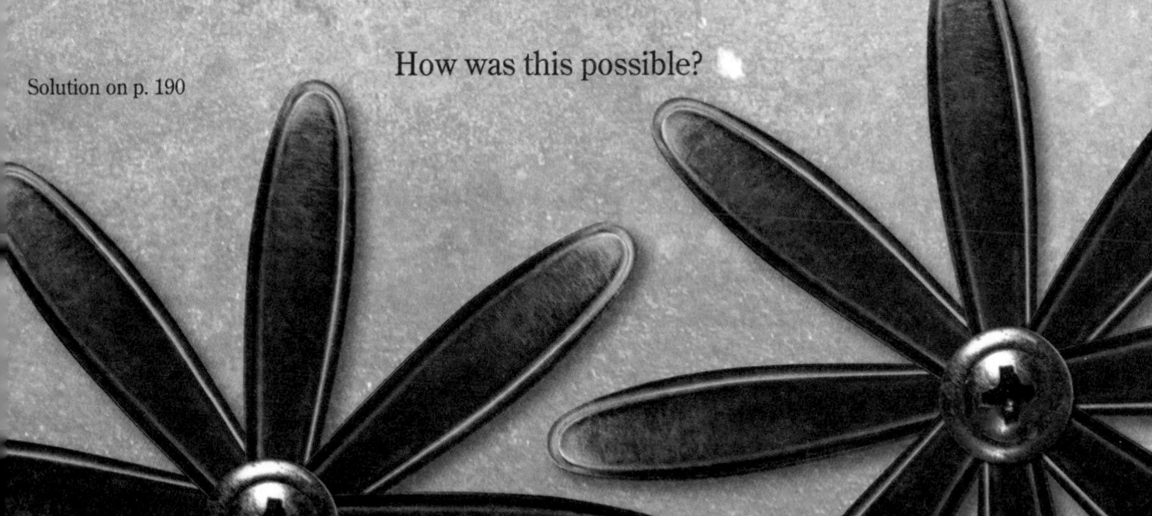

96 BET YOUR HOUSE

Two notoriously unlucky gamblers are in trouble with their bookmaker. Both have run up debts they cannot pay. The bookmaker asks the men if they would like to take on one final wager. They will both be sat down facing each other, and the bookmaker will place a hat on their heads. Their hats will either be black or red, and both hats may be the same colour. The men will be able to see each other's hat but not their own. If at least one of them can immediately guess correctly the colour of his own hat, both will be let off their debts. But if they both guess wrongly, they will both lose their houses, and most likely their jobs and families. The bookmaker warns them that if he sees them giving any signals, they will lose their houses and he will break their legs! The two men consult. Has their luck just changed?

What would you advise them to do?

Solution on p. 190

97 Four triangles

Remove four matches to leave four identical triangles.

Solution on p. 191

98 CROSSING PATHS

Abigail and Agnes have confused their diaries. Abigail thinks she is visiting Agnes today, while Agnes thinks she is visiting Abigail. They both set off on foot for each other's house at 11 am. Abigail walks at 3 km/h. Agnes ambles along at 2 km/h. Which of the two is closer to Abigail's house when they meet each other on the road?

Solution on p. 191

99 Figure this out

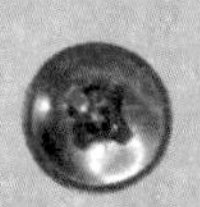

Summing the figures in the number 14, you get 5 (1 + 4).

Summing the figures of 58, you get 13 (5 + 8).

What is the smallest number whose figures sum to 29?

Solution on p. 191

100 ANIMAL MAGIC

How many animals can you see in this picture?

Solution on p. 191

101 A toast

Priscilla the singing telegram has an unusual job tonight. She is hiding inside a giant cake waiting to give a birthday boy a big surprise. Her cue to burst out of the cake and into song will be just after they have finished a toast to the future. Priscilla listens as the toast is proposed. She waits for the guests all to clink their glasses. She counts exactly 55 clinks of crystal, and jumps out of the cake.

How many people were at the party?

Solution on p. 191

102 TRUTH OR LIE

Bill says to Martha:
'I always lie.'

Is Bill lying or is he telling the truth?

Solution on p. 191

103 Making squares

This rectangle is twice as long as it is wide. How would you cut it up so that you could rearrange the pieces into a square?

Solution on p. 192

104 MAKING SQUARES II

Now try something a little harder. This rectangle is five times as long as it is square. Can you cut it up and rearrange it into a square?

Solution on p. 192

105 Changing places

This clock shows the time as a little more than 18 minutes to five. The hands will point at exactly the same places a little after 23 minutes past eight, but the hour hand and the minute hand will have changed places. How many pairs of times are there when the hands of a clock change places between 3 pm and midnight?

Solution on p. 192

106 STRANGE HALVES

If 4 is half of 9, 6 is half of 11
and 7 is half of 12, what is half of 13?

Solution on p. 193

107 SIX SQUARES

Move three matches to make six squares.

Solution on p. 193

108 Money bags

Tyler is on his way to the fair with 139 pound coins. He wants to bag his coins up in such a way that he can pay any amount between 1 and 139 by handing over a combination of bags without looking inside them.

What is the minimum number of bags Tyler will need.

Solution on p. 193

109 Up to a hundred

Insert a mathematical symbol between each number so that the total comes to 100 (you'll also need a pair of brackets):

1?2?3?4?5?6?7?8?9 = 100

Solution on p. 193

110

Heads and feet

Mrs Owen keeps chickens and pigs in her back yard. Between them, her animals have 9 heads and 30 feet.

How many pigs does Mrs Owen have, and how many chickens?

Solution on p. 193

111

Weigh anchor

Clive has taken Mathilda out for a romantic boat trip on the lake. They want to fix their attention just on each other, so they drop the anchor out of the boat to stay put for an hour or so. Does the water level of the lake go up, go down, or stay the same when they do this?

Solution on p. 193

112

Three squares

Move four matches to make three squares.

Solution on p. 194

113 COG COGITATION

Arkwright needs 8 cogs for his new threshing machine as soon as possible. There are two ironmongers in town. Mr Black tells him he can make 1 cog per week. Mr Smith tells him he can manage 3 cogs per week. They will both charge him 1 pound per cog. When is the earliest he can have his 8 cogs?

Solution on p. 194

114 OLYMPIC MEDALLIST

In the 10,000 metres final at the Olympics, Reinhard passed the runner in second place on the penultimate lap. Then Reinhard himself was passed by two runners on the finishing straight. What medal did Reinhard win?

Solution on p. 194

115

WINDY RIDE

Sarah cycles 12 kilometres to work every day. In an effort to keep fit, she always cycles as fast as she can. One day, a strong wind is blowing constantly. Sarah cycles to work with the wind on her back and it takes her 30 minutes. On her way home, struggling into the wind, it takes her 40 minutes. How long does it take Sarah to get to work on days when there is no wind?

Solution on p. 194

116 USE YOUR LOAF

Mrs Maxwell needs to bake her bread for exactly 45 minutes. But all she has are two wicks and a box of matches. She knows that both wicks take exactly one hour to burn all the way down, but she also knows that they burn at irregular rates – in other words, after half an hour, perhaps only one third of the wick will have burned.

How does Mrs Maxwell bake a perfect loaf?

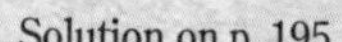

Solution on p. 195

117 ODD AND EVEN

George and Arthur played seven games of badminton on Monday. Each won the same number of games as the other, and no game of badminton can end in a draw.

How did this happen?

Solution on p. 195

118 PRICING MIX

Mrs Smith and Mrs Bramley each sell apples at the market. Mrs Smith sells her apples at 3 for a penny, Mrs Bramley hers at 2 for a penny. At the end of the day, they both have 30 apples left and Mrs Bramley has to go home. Mrs Smith agrees to sell the rest of Mrs Bramley's apples for her. To make things easier, Mrs Smith mixes the apples together and sells them at a price of 5 for 2 pence.

Mrs Smith is going to lose out on this deal. Why?

Solution on p. 195

UP THE POWER

119

Replace the letters with numerals to make the following true (each letter represents a different numeral):

$$B^C = CLIMB$$

Solution on p. 195

LOSE A SQUARE

120

Turn these five squares into four by moving two matches.

Solution on p. 195

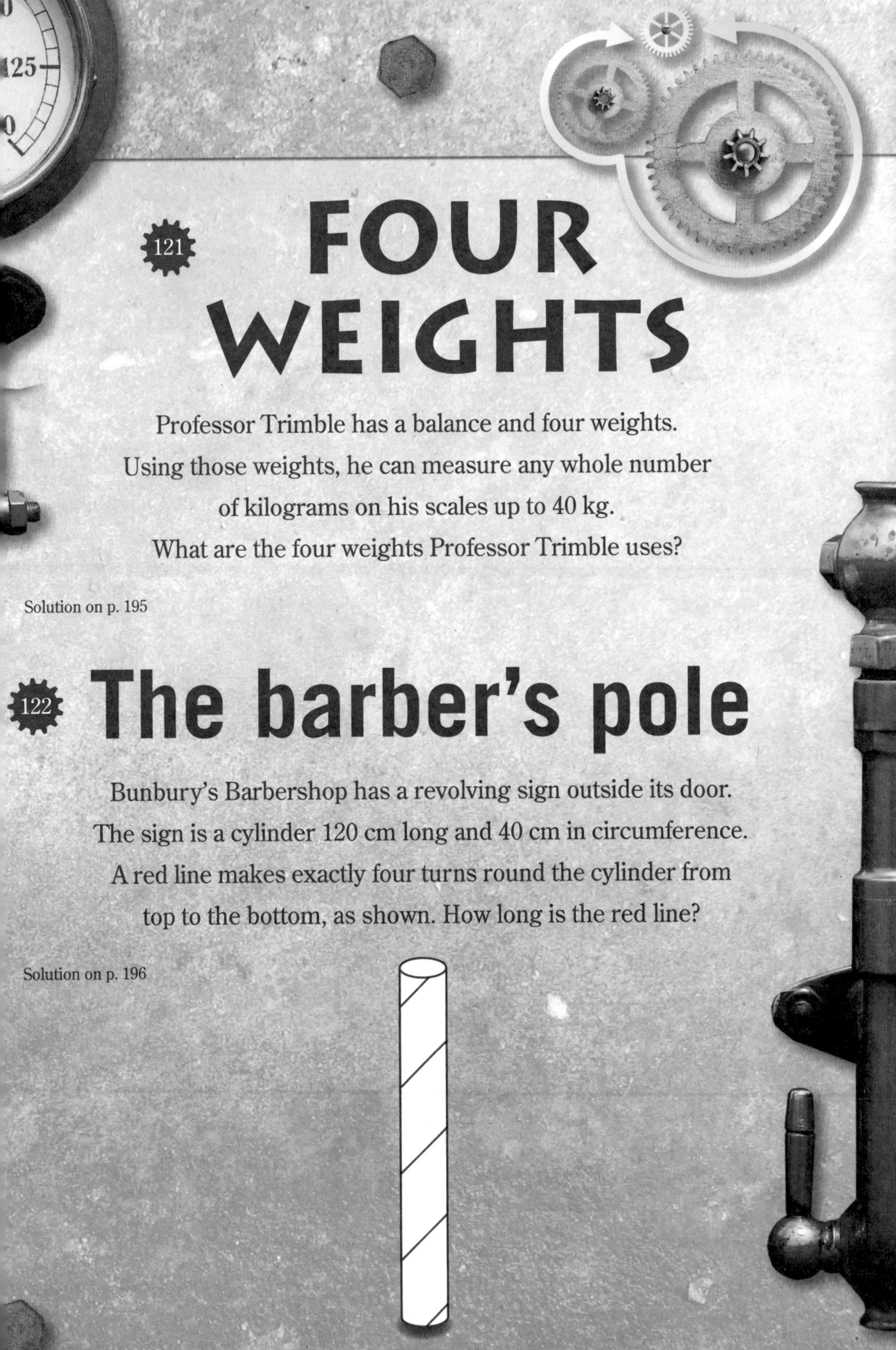

121 FOUR WEIGHTS

Professor Trimble has a balance and four weights. Using those weights, he can measure any whole number of kilograms on his scales up to 40 kg. What are the four weights Professor Trimble uses?

Solution on p. 195

122 The barber's pole

Bunbury's Barbershop has a revolving sign outside its door. The sign is a cylinder 120 cm long and 40 cm in circumference. A red line makes exactly four turns round the cylinder from top to the bottom, as shown. How long is the red line?

Solution on p. 196

123 CAT TIMES CAT

Replace the letters with numerals (0–9) to make the equation work (each letter represents a different numeral):

$$CAT = (C + A + T) \times C \times A \times T$$

Solution on p. 196

124 BULBS IN THE BASEMENT

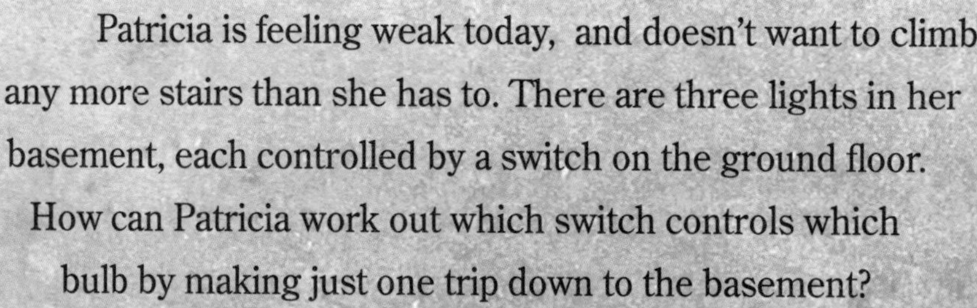

Patricia is feeling weak today, and doesn't want to climb any more stairs than she has to. There are three lights in her basement, each controlled by a switch on the ground floor. How can Patricia work out which switch controls which bulb by making just one trip down to the basement?

Solution on p. 196

125 BOY AND GIRL

A boy and a girl sit next to each other in class. 'I am a boy,' says the child with blue eyes. 'I am a girl,' says the child with brown eyes. Their teacher knows that at least one of them is lying. Which is the boy and which is the girl?

Solution on p. 196

NINE SQUARES

Move eight matches to make nine squares.

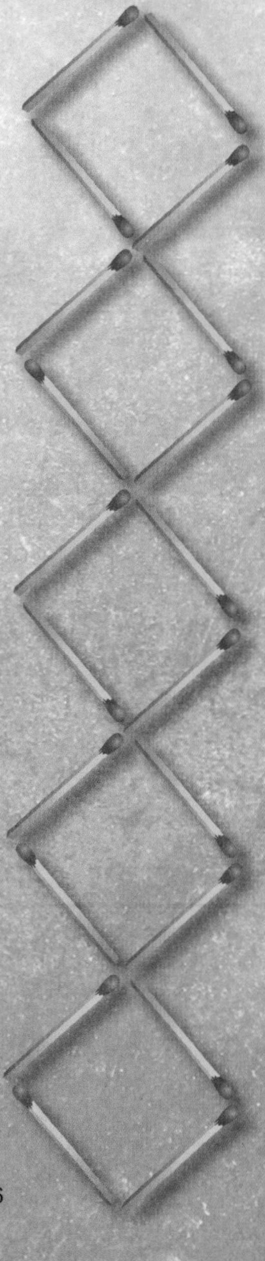

Solution on p. 196

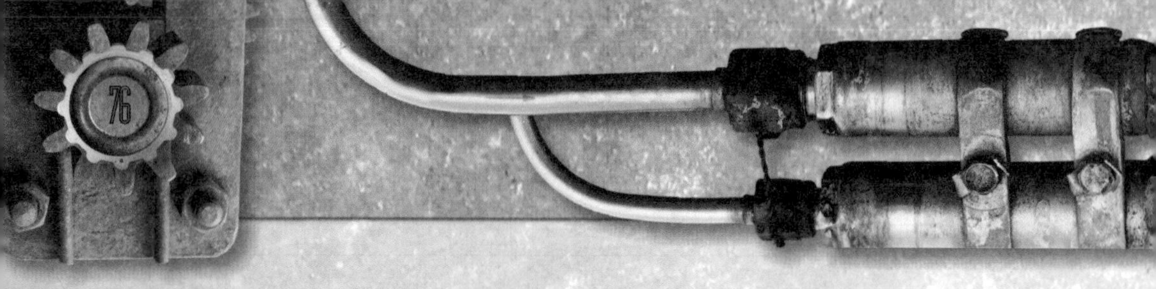

127 A KING'S DILEMMA

A prisoner is brought before a bloodthirsty king and told he is to be executed at dawn. The king tells him, 'You must make a statement. If I deem that statement to be true, you will be hanged. If I deem it to be false, you will face the firing squad.'

The prisoner makes his statement, and the king decides he has to let him go.

What did the prisoner say?

Solution on p. 197

128 Sum to 1000

How would you make 1000 using only the figure 8 and the mathematical operation addition?

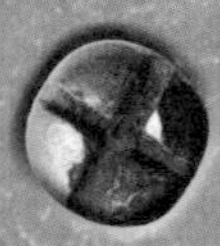

Solution on p. 197

129 *Census time*

A census taker asks Mr Smith at the doorway to his house:
'How many children do you have, and what are their ages?'
Mr Smith replies:
'I have three daughters. If you multiply their ages together, you get the number of the house next door.'

The census taker goes next door to number 36, but comes back a moment later and tells Mr Smith that she needs more information. Mr Smith replies, agitated,
'I have to go now. My eldest is calling me.'

The census taker thanks Mr Smith. She now knows the ages of his daughters.

How old are Mr Smith's daughters?

Solution on p. 197

130 BETWEEN 4 AND 9

What mathematical symbol can you place between 4 and 9 to produce a number that is bigger than 4 but smaller than 9?

Solution on p. 197

131 THREE SHIRTS

Three friends, Mr Red, Mr Blue and Mr Black, meet for dinner. One man is wearing a red shirt, the second a blue shirt and the third a black shirt. One of the friends remarks, 'Have you noticed how we're all wearing shirts of a different colour from our names?'

The man in the black shirt replies,

'Yes, Mr Blue, you're quite right!'

Which man is wearing which shirt?

Solution on p. 197

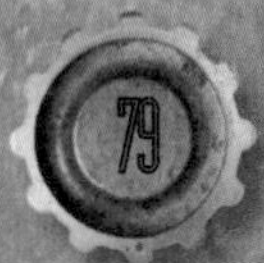

132 NAILED ON

A carpenter fixes a square metal plate measuring 48 cm by 48 cm to a wooden board in such a way that there are 25 nails on each side of the square. Each nail is the same distance from its neighbours.

How many nails does the carpenter use?

Solution on p. 197

133 Matching sum

Can you correct this equation by moving just one match?

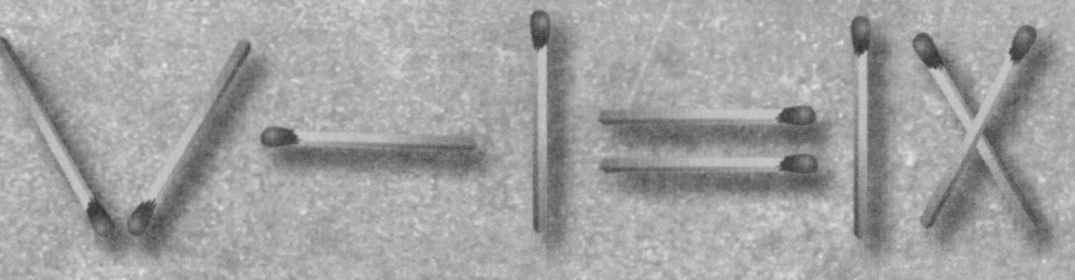

Solution on p. 197

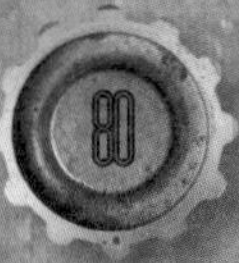

134 FOOTBALL LEAGUE

The football teams in the Kent Senior League play each of the other teams once at home and once away in a full League season. There are 56 matches in total during the season.

How many teams are there in the Kent Senior League?

Solution on p. 198

135 Door to freedom

A man is imprisoned in a cell with two doors. The doors are unlocked, but a guard stands in front of each of them. The prisoner knows that one door leads to freedom, while the other leads to the dungeon and a lifetime of imprisonment. He can leave the cell and go through either door, but he cannot then turn back. One of the guards always tells the truth, while the other always lies. The man is allowed to ask one guard one question, but is not allowed to ask which one is the liar.

What question should he ask to secure his freedom?

Solution on p. 198

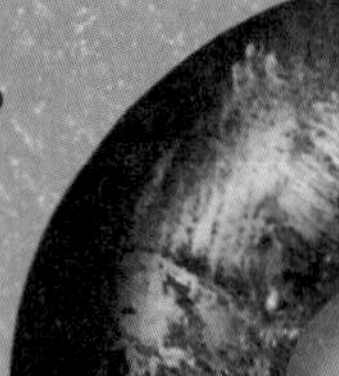

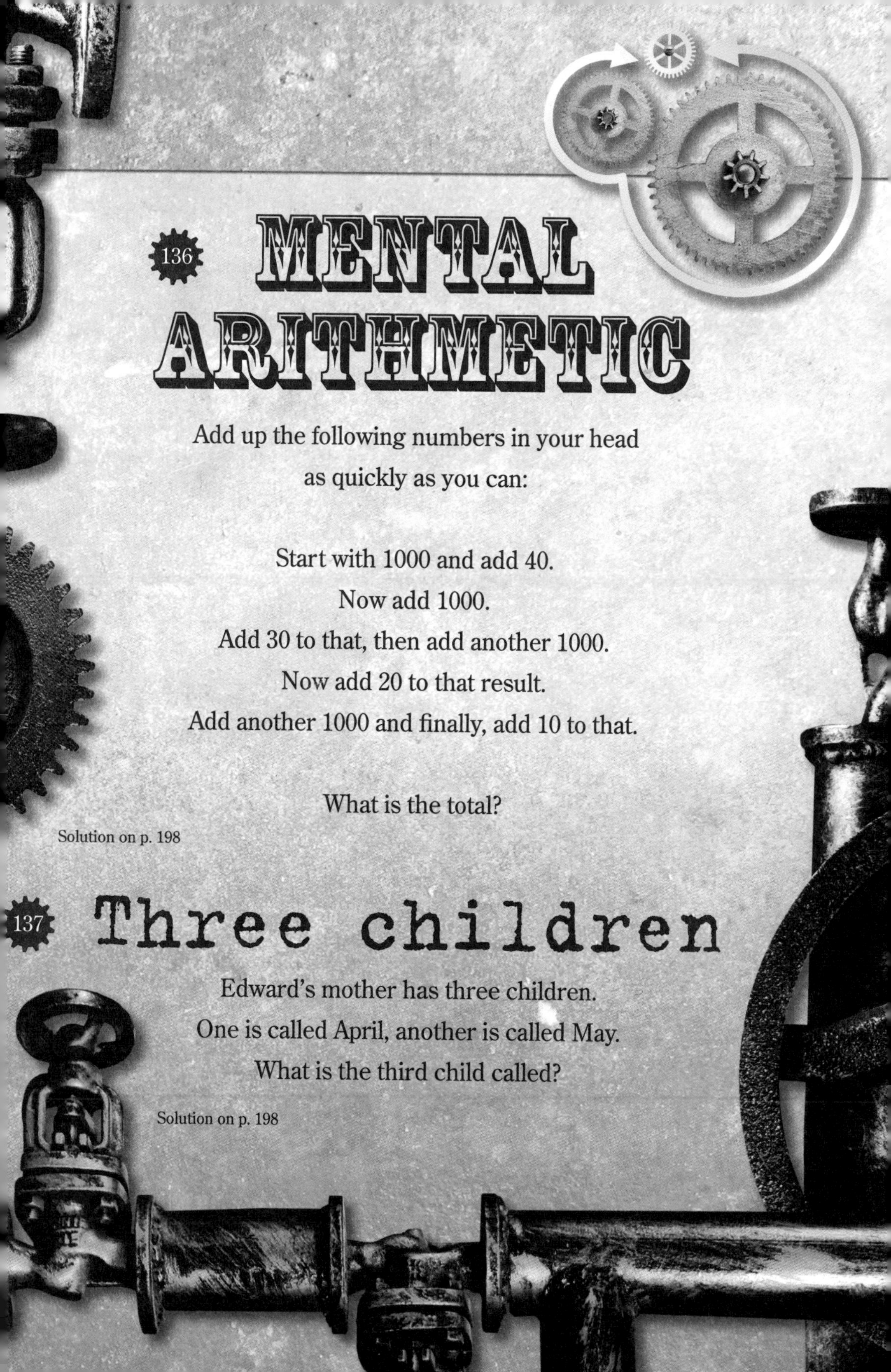

136 MENTAL ARITHMETIC

Add up the following numbers in your head
as quickly as you can:

Start with 1000 and add 40.
Now add 1000.
Add 30 to that, then add another 1000.
Now add 20 to that result.
Add another 1000 and finally, add 10 to that.

What is the total?

Solution on p. 198

137 Three children

Edward's mother has three children.
One is called April, another is called May.
What is the third child called?

Solution on p. 198

138 FRANKENSTEIN'S BLOOD

Dr Frankenstein is measuring out some new blood for his monster. He has a large flask filled with blood that has a capacity of 8 litres (flask C), and two empty flasks with capacities of 3 and 5 litres, respectively (flasks A and B).

How can he measure exactly 4 litres of blood?

Solution on p. 198

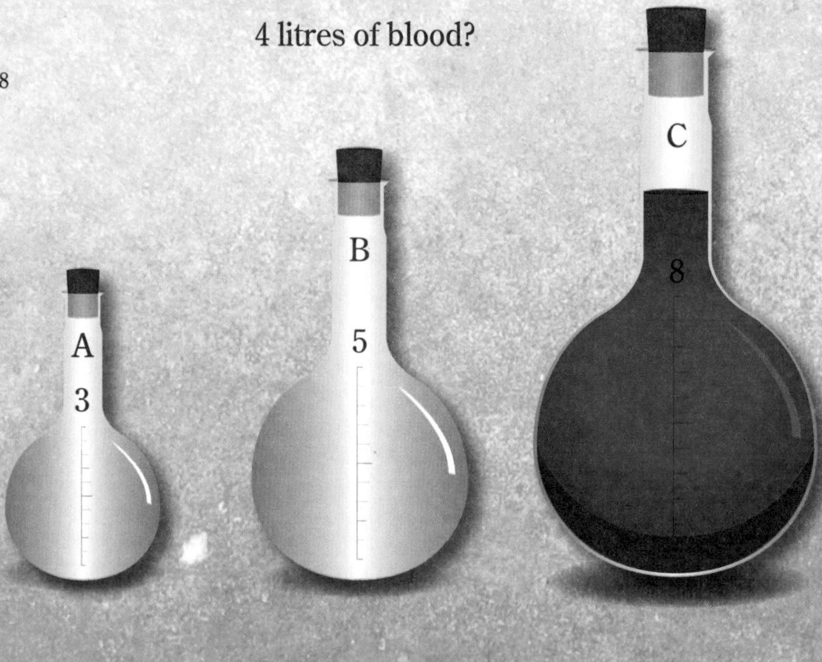

139 Six triangles

Remove three matches to leave six identical triangles.

Solution on p. 198

140 ISLAND OF FIRE

A man is stranded on an island covered in woodland and surrounded by cliffs. One day, disaster strikes and a fire starts on the west end of the island. The wind is blowing from the west, and soon the whole island will be burned, killing everything in its path. The man cannot put out the fire, so how does he survive it?

Solution on p. 199

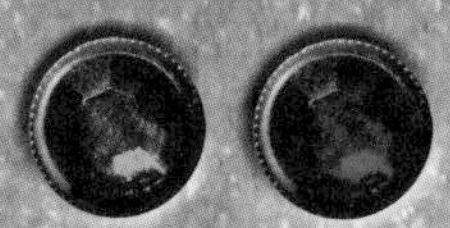

CIRCULAR ROOF

If the blue rectangle in the corner of the observatory measures 6 m by 12 m, what is the diameter of its circular roof?

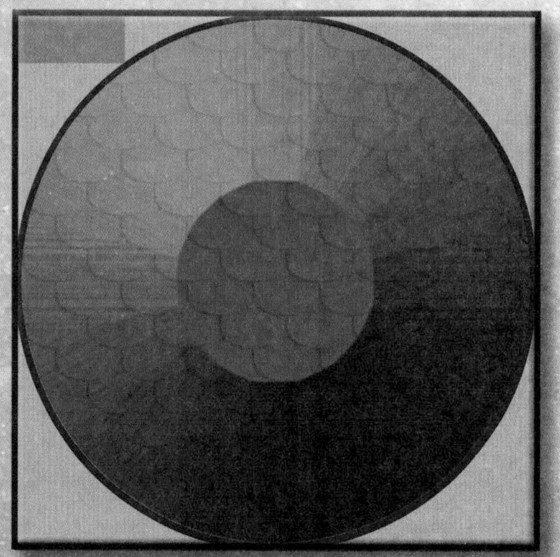

Solution on p. 199

Class treat

Mrs Jenkins has brought a tin of sweets along to class. There are 24 children in her class and 24 sweets in the tin. The children all want a sweet, but they also want Mrs Jenkins to leave at least one sweet in the tin. How does she keep her class happy?

Solution on p. 199

143

What is the next number in the sequence:

0, 1, 1, 2, 3, 5, 8, 13, 21, ??

Solution on p. 199

144 Three figures

Which of these three figures is the largest?

Solution on p. 199

145 Appearing area

Both these figures are made of the same four parts.
So where has the extra area marked 'A' come from?

A

Solution on p. 200

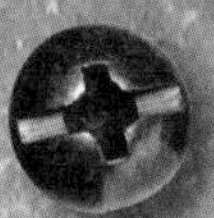

146 Nine triangles

Draw three straight lines on this figure to make nine triangles.

Solution on p. 200

147 CHOCOLATE SQUARES

Arnold has a bar of chocolate that is eight squares long and four squares wide. How many times does he have to break the chocolate so that all the squares are separate pieces? (He can only break one piece of chocolate at a time, and must break it horizontally or vertically.)

Solution on p. 200

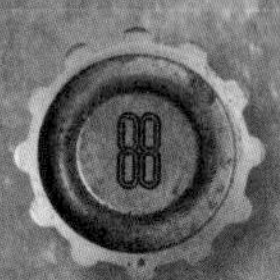

ROUND THE WORLD

The circumference of the earth is 40,000 km. Imagine you have a very long rope, which is tied around the middle of the earth at the equator, touching its surface. Then the rope is raised onto the ends of 1 metre-high poles all around its length. How much longer does the rope need to be so that it still reaches right around the circumference?

Solution on p. 200

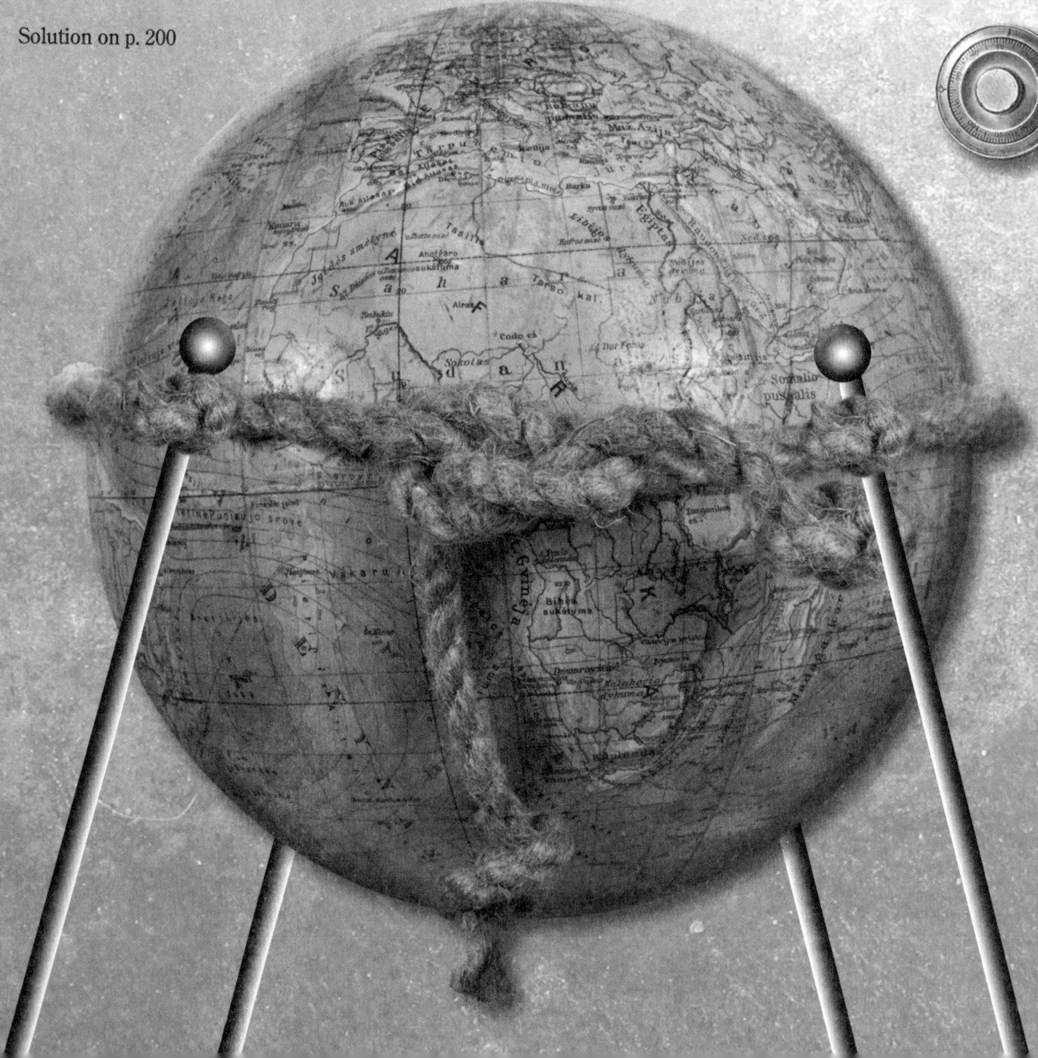

149 MATCH BRIDGE

Using just four matches, can you build a bridge between the two matchboxes?

Solution on p. 200

150 PAYDAY

Oliver and Arnold are walking home from the factory on payday, and each has the same amount of money as the other. How many pounds must Oliver give to Arnold so that Arnold has 10 pounds more than Oliver?

Solution on p. 201

151 MONEY

Replace the letters with numerals (0–9) to make this equation work (each letter represents a different numeral):

SEND + MORE = MONEY

Solution on p. 201

152 TEN PRISONERS

Ten dangerous prisoners are being held together in a large, round cell. The gaoler needs to erect three circular electric fences inside the cell to separate all the prisoners from each other. Where should he put them?

Solution on p. 201

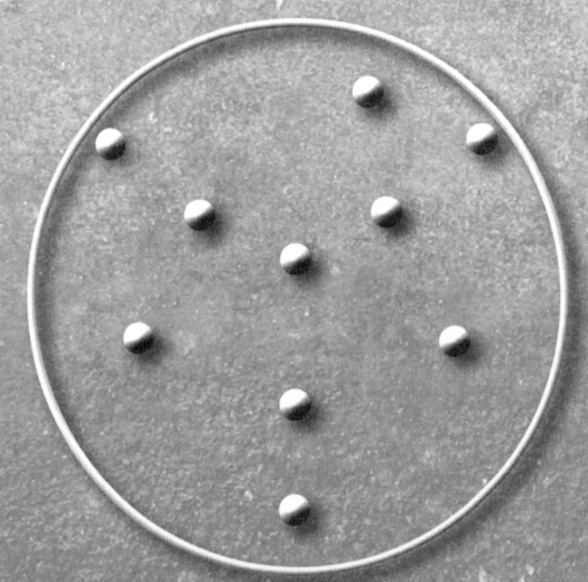

153

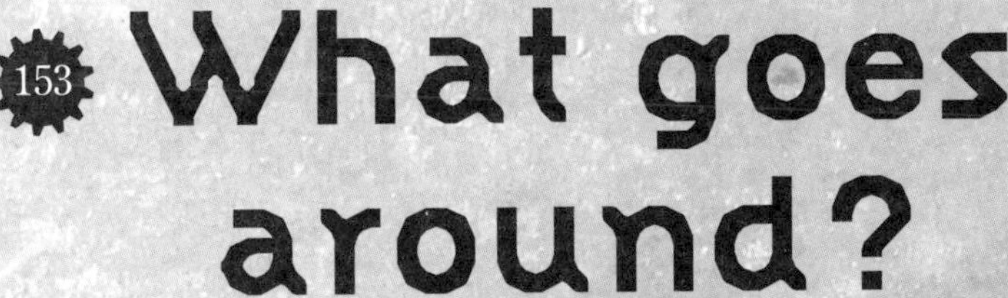

Which of the two small circles is perfectly round?

Solution on p. 201

154 FOUR TAPS

Boston's new municipal swimming pool has four taps. On its own, the first tap takes 12 hours to fill the pool, the second tap takes 5 hours, the third tap 10 hours and the fourth tap 6 hours. How long does it take to fill the pool using all four taps at once?

Solution on p. 201

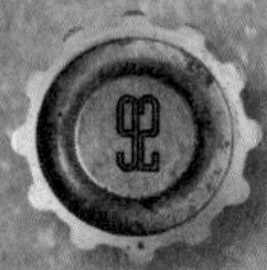

155 Something fishy

Move three matches to make the fish below swim to the left.

Solution on p. 201

156 How many eggs?

Mrs Thomas was not happy. Her daughter Caroline had returned from the grocer with a box of very small eggs. 'I only paid 12 pence for the lot,' explained Caroline. 'The grocer threw in two extra because they were small. So they cost 1 penny less per dozen than the price he had first offered.'

How many eggs did Caroline buy?

Solution on p. 202

157

PUZZLING SCALES

Owen the palaeontologist is weighing his fossilized shell. How many marbles does the shell weigh if the top two scales are balanced? (There are 12 marbles in the top scales, 8 in the middle.)

Solution on p. 202

158 DRIVING TEST

Karl Benz wants to prove how good his new Motorwagen is by outrunning a horse-drawn carriage. He drives it at 16 km/h, which is the car's top speed, and overtakes a carriage travelling at a constant 8 km/h. How long must Benz keep on driving until he can stop for 15 minutes to let the engine cool down and start off again before he is overtaken by the carriage?

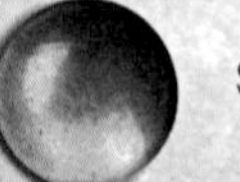

Solution on p. 202

159 A happy divorce

Barnabus and Florence are in love with each other.
They have been married for 20 years.
Barnabus tells Florence that he wants a divorce.
Florence is delighted.

Why?

Solution on p. 202

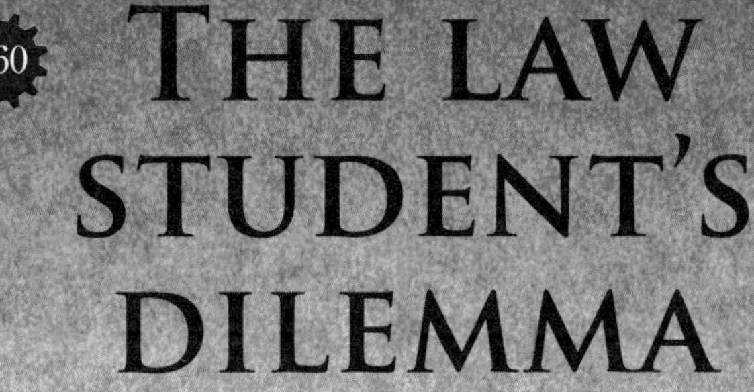

160 THE LAW STUDENT'S DILEMMA

Here is a paradox from Ancient Greece.

The teacher Protagoras agrees to take the penniless Euthalus as his student on condition that Euthalus pays him for his tuition upon winning his first court case. Later, impatient for his money, Protagoras sues Euthalus for it, even though Euthalus has not yet won a case. Protagoras argues that if he wins the case, he will be owed the money, and that if Euthalus wins the case, he is still owed the money on the terms of the original contract. Euthalus, on the other hand, claims that if Protagoras wins the case, Euthalus still hasn't won a case, so he cannot be due to pay. If Euthalus wins the case, the terms of the original contract are voided, so he still does not have to pay.

Who is right, Protagoras or Euthalus?

Solution on p. 202

161 Six triangles

Move two matches to leave six triangles.

Solution on p. 202

162 BLANK FACE

The ever-forgetful Professor Meade looked blankly for a second at the man standing in front of him. He reminded himself, 'The son of this man is the father of my son.'

Who was Professor Meade looking at?

Solution on p. 203

163 Buffon's matches

French mathematician the Comte de Buffon worked out this puzzle. Draw a row of parallel lines on the floor that are two match-lengths apart. Now drop a whole box-worth of matches, one by one, randomly on the area with the lines. After doing this, count the number of matches that lie across a line, and divide the total number of matches by this number.

What is the most likely result?

Solution on p. 203

164 HOW OLD?

Andrea is half of her mother's age. Ten years ago, she was one-third of her mother's age.

How old is Andrea?

Solution on p. 203

165 Circular sums

Substitute a number between 1 and 9 for each star so that the sum of the numbers in each circle is the same.

Solution on p. 203

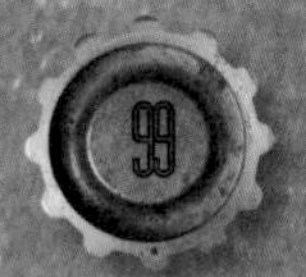

166 A HAPPY OFFICE

Mr Mainwaring is rearranging the clerks' desks at the bank. But he has a problem. Mr Coltart wants to sit behind Miss Armitage, but Miss Armitage insists on sitting behind Mr Coltart.

How does Mr Mainwaring keep both his clerks happy?

Solution on p. 203

THE MISSING POUND

Three weary travellers book into a hotel for the night. They are told that it will cost them £10 each, so they hand over £30 and get settled in. Later, the desk clerk realizes that he should only have charged them £25 as they had agreed to share the triple room. He gives the bellboy £5 to refund the travellers, but the bellboy is dishonest and pockets £2, refunding just £1 each to the travellers. So the travellers spent £27 pounds and the bellboy kept £2. Where did the missing pound go?

Solution on p. 203

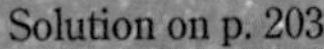

168 A CABIN CONUNDRUM

In a small cabin in the woods, two men lie dead. The cabin itself is not burned, but the forest all around is burned to cinders.

How did the men die?

Solution on p. 203

169 THE LORRY AND THE PIGEON

A fully laden lorry weighing exactly 20 tonnes starts across a 10-km bridge that can only safely hold vehicles that are exactly 20 tonnes or less in weight. Half way across the bridge, a pigeon weighing 500 g lands on the lorry. The bridge does not collapse.

Why not?

Solution on p. 204

170 Two children

Walking along the street one day, Mr Bartholomew remarked to a lady playing with two children of different ages, 'What beautiful children you have.' One of the children was a girl.

What are the chances that both children were girls?

Solution on p. 204

171 Three squares

Move three matches to make three squares.

Solution on p. 204

172 *Plane crash*

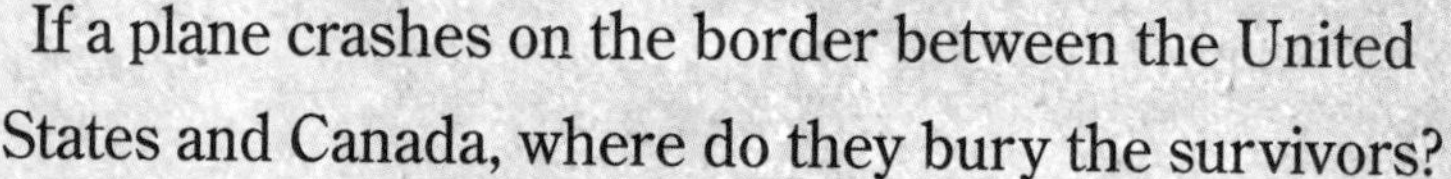

If a plane crashes on the border between the United States and Canada, where do they bury the survivors?

Solution on p. 204

173 SIX GLASSES

Mr Overend has lined up six wine glasses in a row in front of him. The first three are filled with wine. The second three are empty. How can he make the row alternate between empty and full glasses by only moving one glass?

Solution on p. 204

177 EQUAL AREAS

Add four matches to divide the square into two parts of equal area and shape. You may not overlap or break the matches.

Solution on p. 205

178 Tunnelling test

A kilometre-long train travelling at 60 km/h enters a kilometre-long tunnel. How long does it take for the entire train to pass through the tunnel?

Solution on p. 205

179 THE WASON TEST

These four cards are placed in front of you on a table. Each has a number on one side and a colour on the other. Which cards should you turn over to prove the truth of the following statement: If a card shows an even number on one face, then its opposite face is red?

Solution on p. 205

180 Two drunk men

Two drunkards, Dum and Dee, stumble across a cask of wine with its lid removed on their way home. Peering into the cask, Dum the optimist thinks it is just over half full. Dee the pessimist thinks it is just over half empty. How can they find out who is right?

Solution on p. 206

184 TRIANGLE AND A DIAMOND

Move two matches to make a triangle and a diamond.

Solution on p. 206

185 Popping pills

Mrs Fontague is feeling very ill. Her doctor prescribes her 10 pills, one to be taken immediately, and the rest taken one at a time every quarter of an hour after that. How long will it take Mrs Fontague to finish her pills?

Solution on p. 206

186 Off to market

As she strolled to market with nothing but an empty basket, Mrs Tyler met seven farmers. Each farmer had three pigs. Three of the farmers had two sheep each. And one of the farmers had 15 geese.

How many feet were walking to market?

Solution on p. 206

187 Cue power

A snooker player wants to take his own cue to a tournament on an island resort, but his cue is nearly 150 cm long, and the ferry rules don't allow luggage more than 120 cm long. The player goes to see a carpenter, who makes him a new case for his cue out of very thin wood. The snooker player is allowed on the ferry with his cue, carrying it in its new case.

What shape is the case?

Solution on p. 207

188

Four of a kind

From a full deck of 52 cards, how many cards do you need to draw to guarantee you have four of a kind in your hand?

Solution on p. 207

189

Five decks

Now, if you have five decks of cards, how many do you need to draw to guarantee four of a kind?

Solution on p. 207

190 Two balls

Which of the orange circles is bigger?

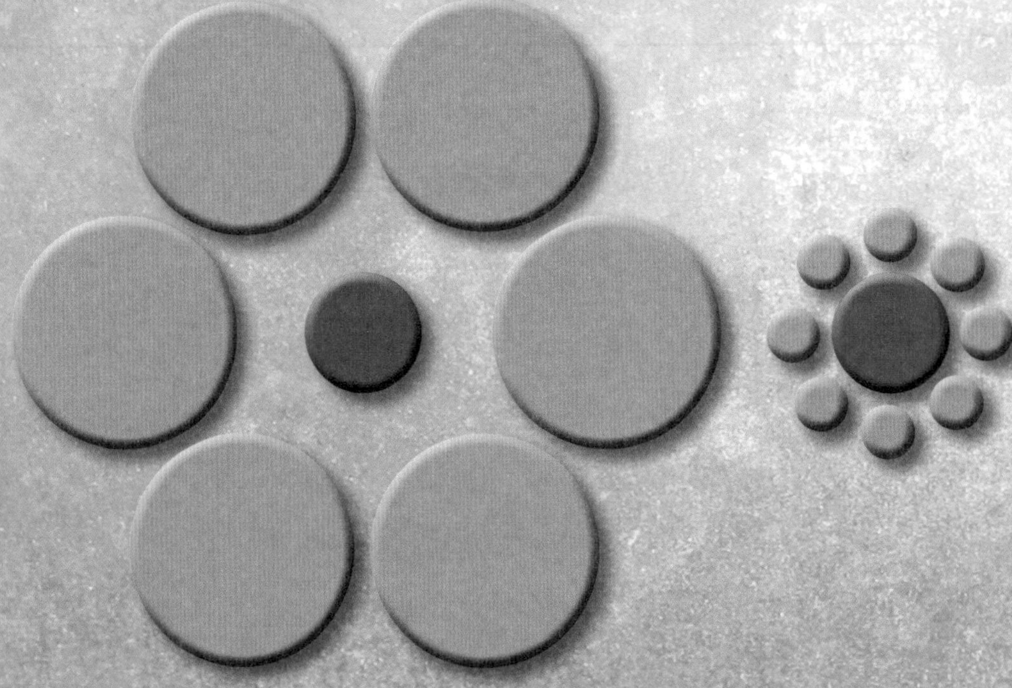

Solution on p. 207

191 MAKE A THIRD

Arrange the numerals 1, 2, 3, 4, 5, 6, 7, 8 and 9, using each just once, to create a fraction equal to ⅓.

Solution on p. 207

192 BREAK THE CHAIN

A jewellery maker wants to make one long silver chain out of four separate chains three links long. Every link she breaks she will have to solder back together again. How can she make her long chain with the minimum of soldering?

Solution on p. 207

193

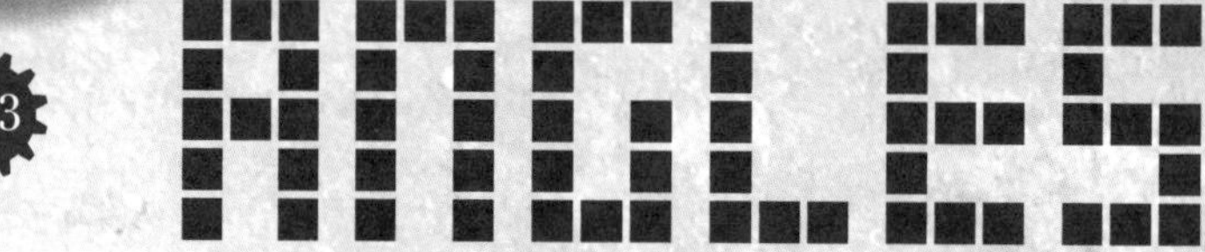

What is the angle formed by the two dotted lines drawn on the sides of this cube?

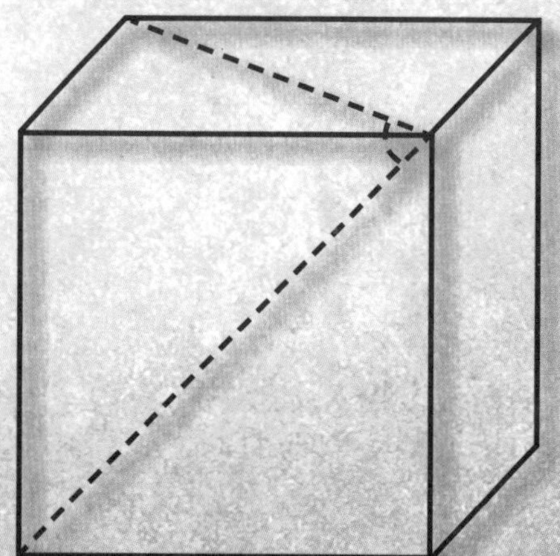

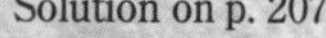

Solution on p. 207

194 TEN BALLS

Place these ten balls in five lines so that each line has four balls on it.

Solution on p. 208

195 DIAMOND DILEMMA

Mr Fulbright the gemologist has three diamonds and two boxes. One of the boxes is twice as long and twice as wide as the other. How can he put the diamonds in the boxes in such a way that each box contains an odd number of diamonds?

Solution on p. 208

196 FIVE 5s

Replace the ?s with mathematical symbols to make this equation work (you can add parentheses, too):

5 ? 5 ? 5 ? 5 ? 5 = 100

Solution on p. 208

197 AGE CONCERN

Roger is ten times as old as his son, Matthew,
who is four times as old as his sister Theresa.
In 38 years' time, Roger will be twice as old as Theresa.

How old is Roger?

Solution on p. 208

198 WHAT TIME IS IT?

If it were two hours later, it would be half as long
until midnight as it would be if it were an hour later.

What time is it now?

Solution on p. 208

199 STRANGE EQUATION

How would you make this equation correct without changing it?

XI + I = X

Solution on p. 208

200 Slicing problem

This large cube in made of 3 x 3 x 3 smaller cubes. How many times would you have to slice the large cube to completely separate all 27 of the smaller cubes?

Solution on p. 208

201 THREE CHESTS

Mr Prowse presents his students with a puzzle each week. Get it right, and they can play a game of their choice. Get it wrong, and they have to do hard sums of his choice! This week, Mr Prowse shows his class three chests.

'In one of the chests,' says Mr Prowse, 'are gold coins. In another chest are silver coins. And in the third chest are bronze coins. The chests are labelled "gold", "silver" and "gold or silver", but all the labels are wrong. Now tell me, which chest contains which coins?'

Can you help Mr Prowse's students?

Solution on p. 208

DIAMONDS

Move four matches to make five diamonds.

Solution on p. 209

Loose change

Hermione has two coins left in her purse. Together they are worth 30 pence. The only coins that exist that are worth less than 30 pence are 1, 2, 5, 10 and 20 pence pieces. If one of the coins is not a 10-pence piece, how much is each of Hermione's coins worth?

Solution on p. 209

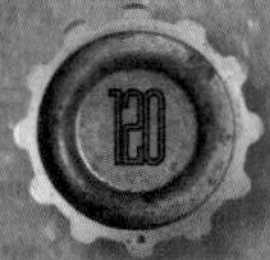

204 Moving pictures

Hold the book in your hands and focus your eyes on the black dot at the centre of this figure. Now move the book towards you, then move it away from you again.

What can you see?

Solution on p. 209

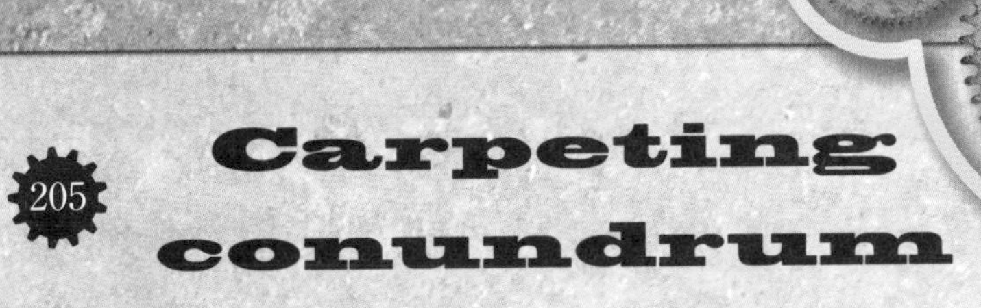

205 Carpeting conundrum

Mrs Williams is designing her dream house. One of the largest rooms in the house measures 9 metres by 12 metres. Mrs Williams wants to split the space up by placing an aquarium measuring 8 m by 1 m in the centre of the room, as shown here. She has a fine Egyptian carpet measuring 10 m by 10 m. How can she cut her carpet into two pieces of the same size that will fit the room perfectly?

Solution on p. 209

206 Mental arithmetic

Divide 30 by ½, then add 20 to the result. What number do you get?

Solution on p. 209

207 *Exam room*

360 school children sit down for their exams. 5 per cent of them have one pen. Of the remaining 95 per cent, half of them have two pens, while the other half have none at all.

How many pens do the children have between them?

Solution on p. 209

208 SENSELESS

Helen is blind, deaf and dumb.
How many of her five senses does she have left?

Solution on p. 209

209 Six squares

Move eight matches to make six squares.

Solution on p. 210

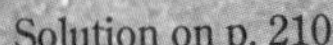

210 CAMPANOLOGY

The bell ringer at Wells Cathedral takes 2 seconds to ring the bells for 3 o'clock. How long does it take her to ring the bells for midday?

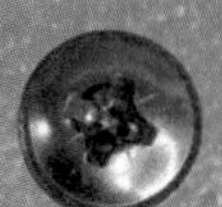

Solution on p. 210

211 THREE SQUARES

Draw these three interlaced squares without lifting your pencil from the paper, without going over any line twice and without crossing over any other line.

Solution on p. 210

212 SUBTRACTION

How many times can you subtract 6 from 36?

Solution on p. 210

213 HAPPY OR SAD

Which of these two fellows looks the happier to you?

Solution on p. 211

214 LAYING TIME

If 600 hens lay on average 600 eggs in eight days, how many eggs do 200 hens lay on average in two days?

Solution on p. 211

215 Touching matches

Arrange these six matches so that each one touches the other five.

Solution on p. 211

216 EASY RIDER

A cowboy rides into Dodge City on Friday.
He stays for two nights, then rides out on Friday.

How?

Solution on p. 211

217 Cleaning windows

William the window cleaner has hit upon hard times. William laments: 'The week before last, I earned less than 3 pounds. Last week I earned only a third as much, and this week I earned less than half as much as last week.' If he charges 25 pence per window cleaned and only charges for whole windows, how much has William earned in the last three weeks?

Solution on p. 211

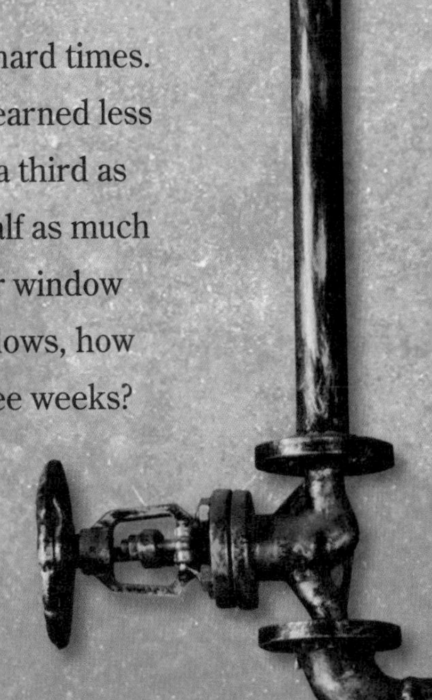

218 SHROEDER'S STAIRCASE

Which way do these stairs lead?

Solution on p. 211

219 STUCK

Replace the letters with numerals to make the following correct (each letter is a different numeral):

$(S + T + U + C + K) \times (S + T + U + C + K) \times (S + T + U + C + K) = STUCK$

Solution on p. 211

220 HENRY'S SPIRAL

The great Edwardian puzzler Henry Dudeney set this challenge. How did he draw this spiral using just a pencil, a pair of compasses and the sheet of paper on which the diagram was made?

Solution on p. 212

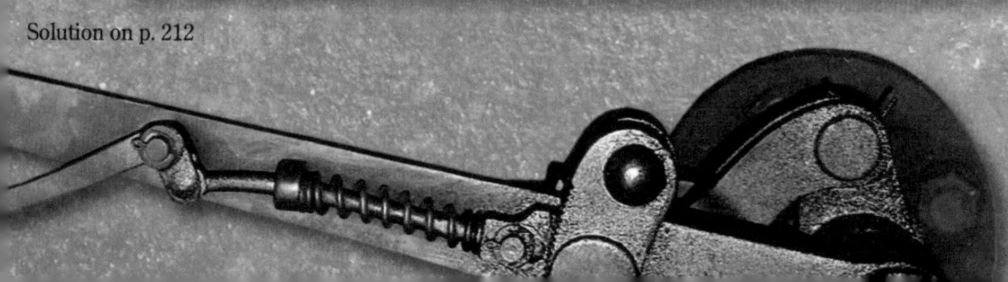

221 CYCLES

A professional cyclist turns onto the motorway, right past a sign saying 'NO CYCLES'. He passes a police car. The policeman sees him, but does nothing. Why did the policeman not pull the professional cyclist over?

Solution on p. 212

222 CORRECT THE EQUATION

Move two matches to make this equation correct.

Solution on p. 212

223 BAKING CAKES

A baker needs to bake three cakes, but he can only fit two cakes in the oven at a time. The cakes need to be baked for two minutes on each side. What is the minimum time the baker needs to bake all three cakes?

Solution on p. 212

224 Number triangle

Place the numbers 1, 2 and 3 in the circles at each corner of the triangle. Now add the numbers 4–9 to the rest of the circles so that each side of the triangle adds up to 17.

Solution on p. 212

225 Find the fake

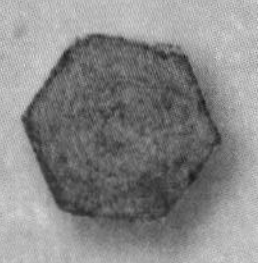

A man has brought 81 rubies to a gemologist for a valuation. The rubies are all the same size, but the man knows that one of them is a fake. He also knows that the fake weighs slightly more than the real jewels. Using this information, how can the gemologist identify the fake ruby using a pair of scales by making just four weighings?

Solution on p. 213

226 ONE LINE

Draw this figure without lifting the pencil from the page, passing along the same route twice or crossing over another line.

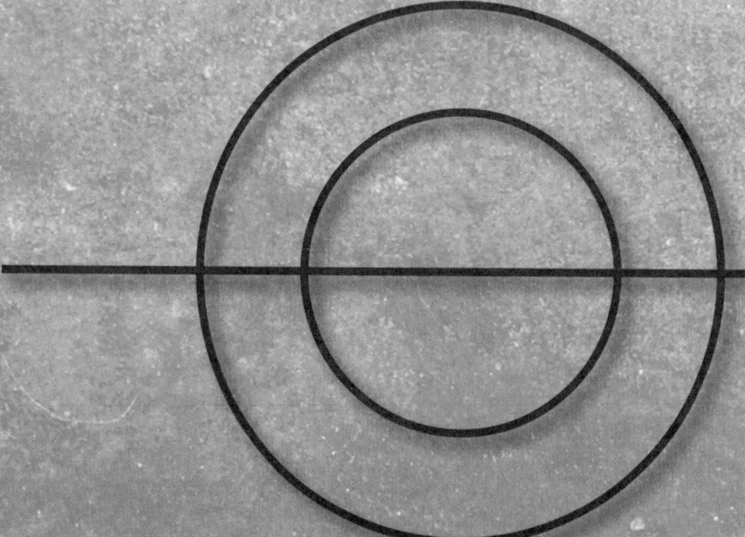

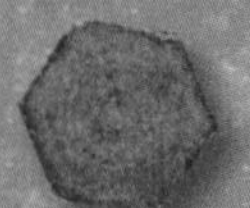

Solution on p. 213

227 # MULTIPLICATION

Enter the numerals 0–9 in the following sum to make it work (3 has already been used and you can use each numeral only once):

3 x . . . . = ...

Solution on p. 213

228 # SEVEN PILLARS

An architect has been commissioned to build Mr Braxton a new country home. The huge house will have a grand ballroom with seven pillars in it. The architect wants to arrange the pillars in such a way that there will be five lines of three pillars.

How does he do this?

Solution on p. 214

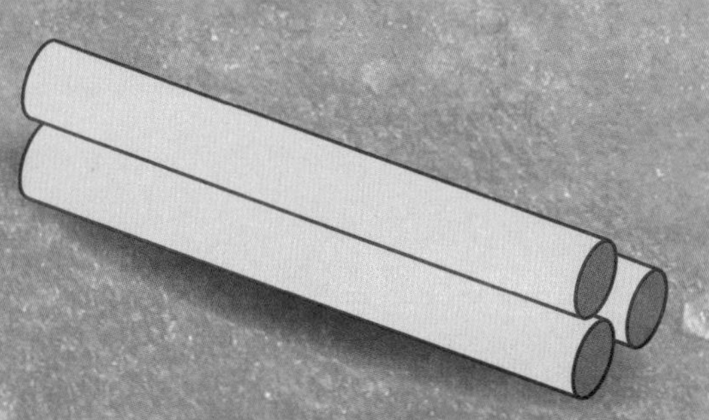

229 TURN OF THE CENTURY

In the year 1900, a woman makes the following calculation: she adds the year she was born to the year her daughter was born, then adds her current age and her daughter's current age.

What number does she come up with?

Solution on p. 214

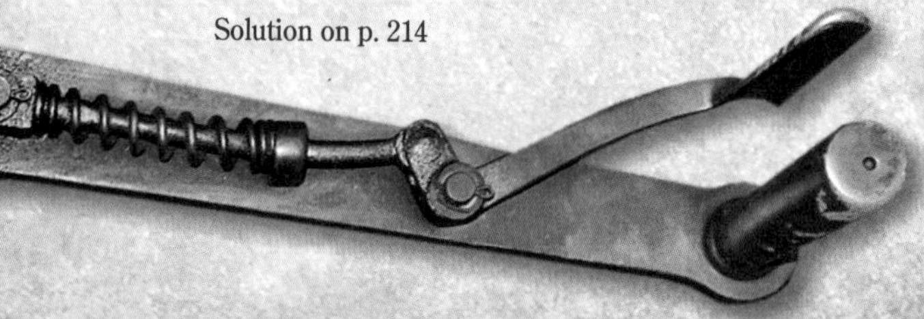

230 THREE COINS

A teacher places three coins in front of her pupil: one copper, one silver and one gold. She tells her pupil: 'If you tell me a true statement, you will be given one of the coins. But if your statement proves to be false, you will be given nothing.'

What should the pupil say to guarantee being given the gold coin?

Solution on p. 214

231 MYSTERY MENU

Five men are staying in a hotel in a strange land where they do not know the language or customs. The hotel always offers the same nine dishes for dinner, listed as A, B, C, D, E, F, G, H and I on the menu. The waiter won't tell them which dish is which letter, and when the dishes are brought out, they are set in the middle of the table in no particular order. If each man orders one dish each per night over three nights, how should they order if they want to work out which dish is represented by each letter?

Solution on p. 214

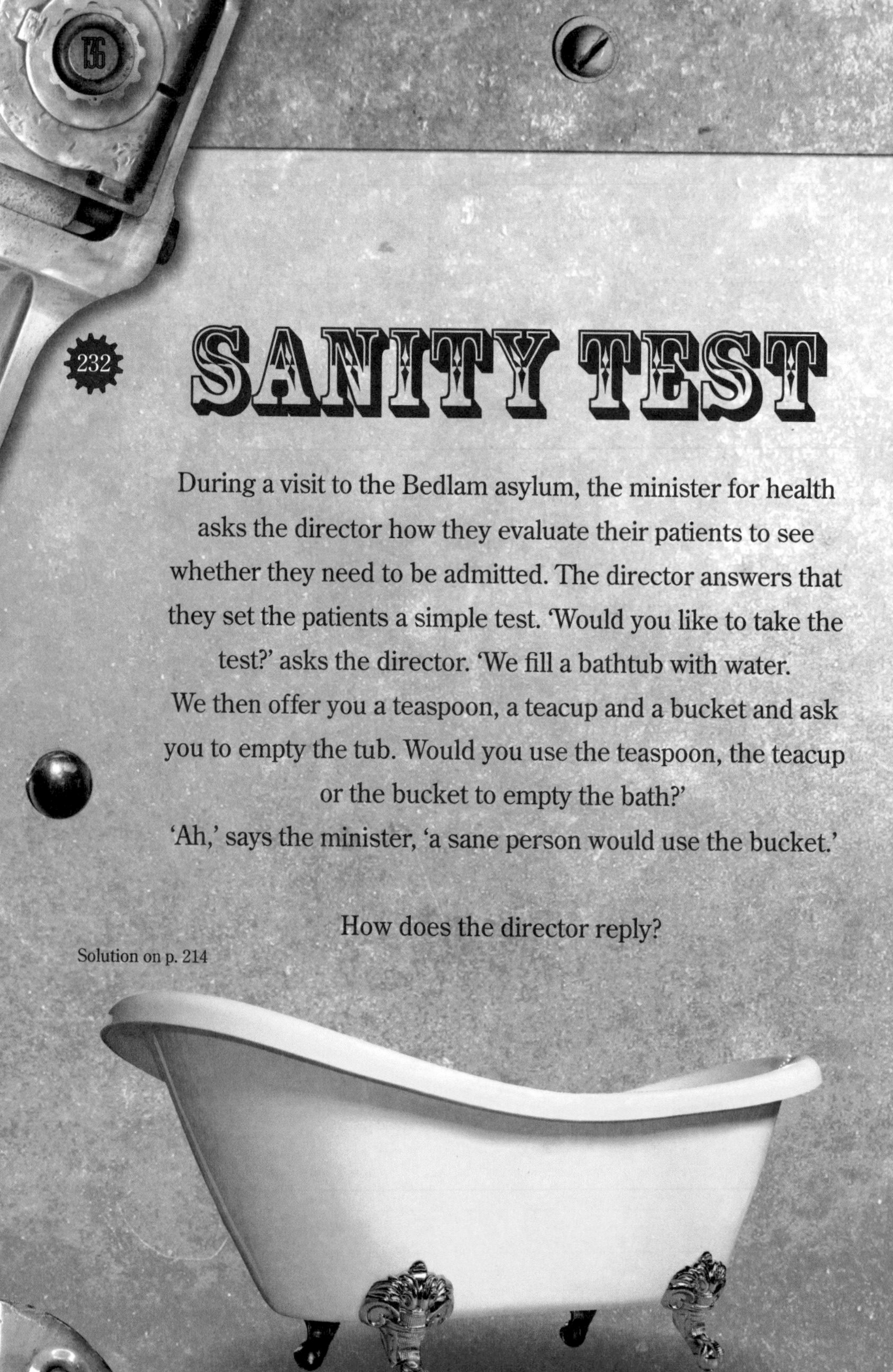

232 SANITY TEST

During a visit to the Bedlam asylum, the minister for health asks the director how they evaluate their patients to see whether they need to be admitted. The director answers that they set the patients a simple test. 'Would you like to take the test?' asks the director. 'We fill a bathtub with water. We then offer you a teaspoon, a teacup and a bucket and ask you to empty the tub. Would you use the teaspoon, the teacup or the bucket to empty the bath?'

'Ah,' says the minister, 'a sane person would use the bucket.'

How does the director reply?

Solution on p. 214

233 Four parts

Divide this shape into four identical parts.

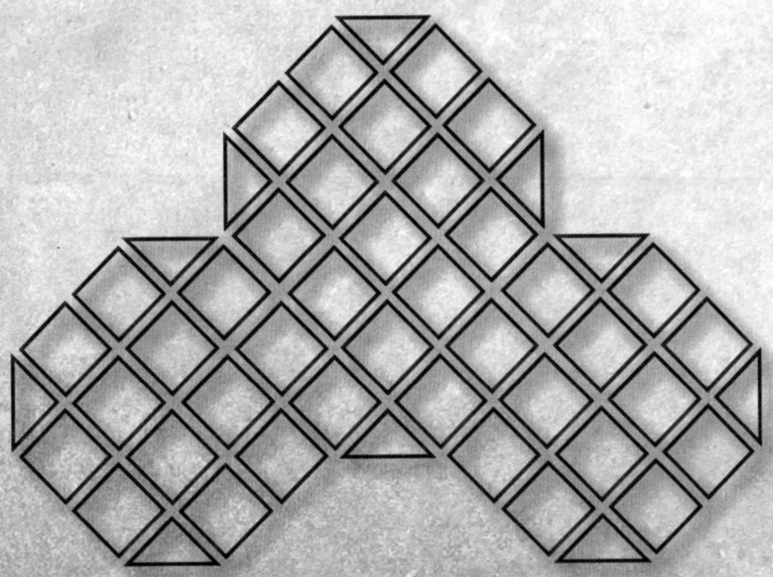

Solution on p. 214

234 Siblings

Mr and Mrs Trevellian have four daughters.
Each of their daughters has one brother.

How many children do the Trevellians have?

Solution on p. 215

235 Five squares

Remove four matches to leave five squares.

(There are two possible answers.)

Solution on p. 215

236 MOVE A FIGURE

Move one of the figures in the following equation to make it correct:

101 - 102 = 1

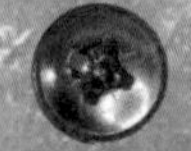

Solution on p. 215

237 BLIND MAN'S DECK

A blind man is handed a deck of 52 cards. He is told that ten of the cards are face up, the rest are face down. How can he divide the cards into two piles and ensure that each pile has the same number of cards facing up?

Solution on p. 215

238 I.T.

The computer and games console below both need to be connected up to the hi-fi, the internet and the mains, as shown. Connect them up in such a way that the cables do not touch or cross.

Solution on p. 215

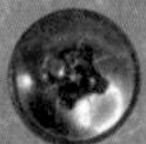

239 Pen and ink

A pen and ink pot together cost 22 pounds.
The pen is worth 20 pounds more than the ink pot.

How much does the pen on its own cost?

Solution on p. 215

240 Wheeler Dealer

At Norwich market, a trader buys a roll of cloth for 60 pounds, then sells it for 70 pounds. Later in the day, he buys the same roll back for 80 pounds and sells it again for 90 pounds.

Was that a wise thing to do?

Solution on p. 215

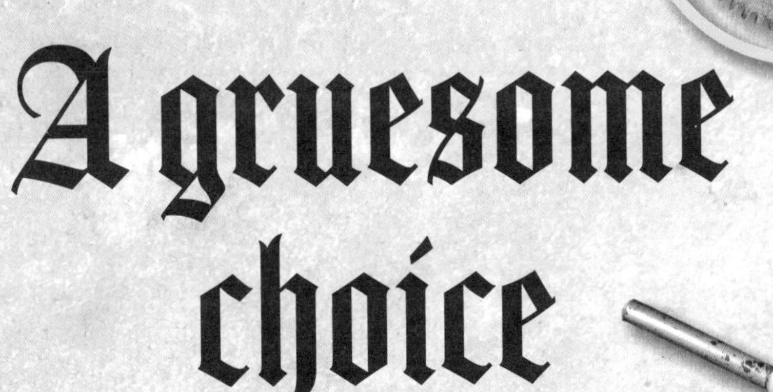

241 A gruesome choice

A condemned man is to be allowed
to choose the manner of his death.
He is given the following six options:

1. Thrown into a deep river tied to a heavy stone.
2. Decapitated by an axe.
3. Eaten alive by a group of cannibals.
4. Thrown into a pit of lions that have not eaten for five months.
5. Hanged by the neck until he is dead.
6. Shot through the heart with a rifle.

Which option should he choose?

Solution on p. 216

242 *How many holes?*

If you fold a piece of paper in half, fold it in half again four more times, then cut off each of the four corners of the resulting rectangle, how many holes will there be when you unfold the paper again?

Solution on p. 216

243 A SQUARE

Make a square by moving one match.
(Think laterally!)

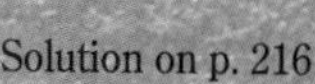
Solution on p. 216

244 Rummy

Emma and Jane are playing rummy in their lunchbreak. They agree to a small wager, and the winner of each round is given a gobstopper by the loser. When the bell goes to return to class, Emma has won two games but Jane is three gobstoppers up.

How many rounds of rummy did they play?

Solution on p. 216

245 EQUAL AREAS

Professor Snipe wants to divide her laboratory into four areas that are the same size and shape.

The plan is below. Can you help?

Solution on p. 216

246 *Will and testament*

Mr Samuels the billionaire has locked his last will and testament inside one of three boxes: a gold box, a sliver box and a lead box. On each box is an inscription. At least one of the inscriptions is true and at least one of them is false.

The inscriptions are:

1. **Gold box**: The will is not in the silver box.
2. **Silver box**: The will is not in this box.
3. **Lead box**: The will is in this box.

His children can open just one box to read the will. If the box is empty, all Mr Samuels' fortune goes to charity.

Which box should they open?

Solution on p. 216

SUBTRACTION

Using the figures 7, 7, 7, 7 and 1, can you make the number 100 using just a minus sign?

Solution on p. 216

Late for work

Arthur leaves for work one morning. Just as he's about to leave, he looks at the time in the mirror. The clock is an analogue clock but doesn't have any numbers on it. Arthur forgets that it is a mirror image and reads the minute hand as the hour hand and the hour hand as the minute hand. He thinks he has plenty of time and strolls to work happily on a 20-minute walk. To his horror, when he gets to work, he finds out that the time is 2½ hours later than the time he saw on his clock.

What time did Arthur leave the house?

Solution on p. 216

249 HOW OLD?

A mother says to her son, 'I am four times as old as you were when I was the same age as you are now.'

If the mother is 40 years old, how old is her son?

Solution on p. 217

250 Moving parts

A sundial is a timepiece with the fewest moving parts: it has no moving parts at all.

Which timepiece has the most moving parts?

Solution on p. 217

251 A NEVER-ENDING GAME

Fed up with the apathy of her class, a teacher devises a game to make them answer her questions. The class is split into three teams: the red, blue and green teams. The teacher will ask questions and the pupils must put their hands up if they know the answer.

If the first pupil to answer correctly is from the red team, one of the blue team will be eliminated. If the correct pupil is from the blue team, one of the green team is eliminated. If they are from the green team, one of the red team is eliminated. The teacher will keep asking questions until only one team is left. Each member of that team will win a chocolate bar.

On hearing this, one clever pupil whispers to her classmates. The questions begin, and to her horror, the teacher finds that none of the pupils wants to answer correctly.

Why?

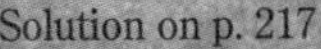

Solution on p. 217

252 Digital clock

Move two matches to make the time half past four.

Solution on p. 217

253 MOUSERS

The hotel housekeeper keeps cats to make sure the kitchens are free of mice. Three cats can catch three mice in three minutes.

How many cats would the housekeeper need to catch 100 mice in 100 minutes?

Solution on p. 218

254 Betting scam

One day, you receive an email from a stranger telling you that he knows of a scam in which horse races are being fixed. To prove it, he predicts the result of a race that day. Sure enough, the 2-1 favourite wins as predicted. The next day, he emails you again saying that there's another fixed race. This time it's a 10-1 outsider, and again the prediction comes true. After a week, you have received six emails correctly predicting the results of six races. A seventh email comes in. The stranger asks, 'Would you like to place a £1,000 bet through me on the next fixed race? We can go halves on the winnings.'

Should you give him your money?

Solution on p. 218

255 WEIGH THE BABY

Standing on the scales holding her baby and her cat, a woman weighs 102 kilograms. If the woman weighs 60 kg more than the combined weight of her baby and her cat, and the cat weighs 60 per cent less than the baby, how much does the baby weigh?

Solution on p. 218

256 Numbers for letters

Replace the letters with numerals to make this work:

ABCD x E = DCBA

Solution on p. 218

257 FAMILY TIES

Annabel has three sisters. All four women are mothers. Her sister Beatrice has two nephews and three nieces. Her sister Carla has one nephew and three nieces. Her sister Davina has one nephew and five nieces. Annabel herself has one daughter and no sons.

How many nephews and nieces does Annabel have?

Solution on p. 218

258 SIX STRAIGHT LINES

How would you draw six straight lines to link these 16 points without lifting the pen from the paper?

Solution on p. 218

259 THINK LATERALLY!

Move one match to make this equation correct.

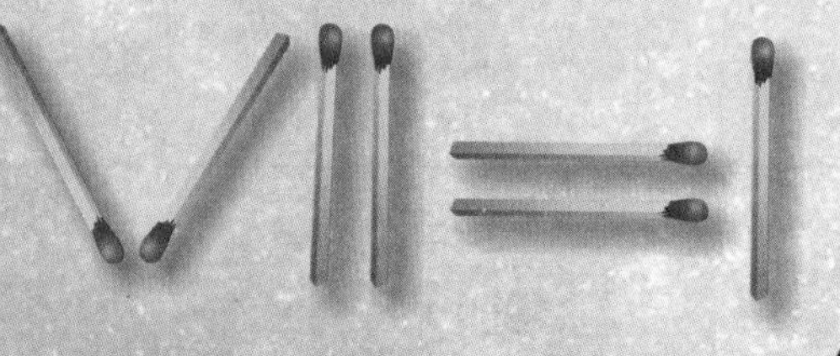

Solution on p. 218

260 A FAIR WEIGHT

A man and his son are carrying a pig to market with its feet all tied together at one point on a pole. The man puts the front of the pole on his shoulder, while and his son takes the back. The distance from shoulder to shoulder is 1.5 metres.

Where should the pig's feet be tied on the pole if it weighs 100 kg, the stronger man should be bearing 60 kg and his boy 40 kg?

Solution on p. 219

261 CLAIRVOYANT

A mystic has been summoned to a haunted house to discover a spirit dwelling there. She can sense that it must be present behind one of four doors, but each door is inscribed with a riddle written by the spirit:

Door A: I'm behind B or C

Door B: I'm behind A or D

Door C: I'm in here

Door D: I'm not in here

The mystic knows that just one of these inscriptions tells the truth.

Where is the spirit?

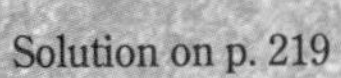
Solution on p. 219

262 Make 24

Using the numbers 5, 5, 5 and 1 once each, make an equation whose result equals 24. You can use the mathematical operations of addition, multiplication, subtraction or division.

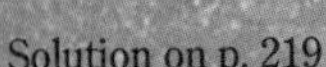
Solution on p. 219

263 Car crash

A man and his son are involved in a terrible car accident. The man dies instantly. The son is very badly injured and is taken to hospital by ambulance. He is rushed to the operating theatre, where the doctor exclaims, 'Oh no, this is my son!'

How can this be?

Solution on p. 219

264 Arrange the numbers

Place the numbers 1–8 in the squares so that no number is in contact on any side or diagonal with any number that is one greater or one less than it. So, for instance, 4 cannot be next to 3 or 5.

Solution on p. 219

265

BEAR HUNTING

A hunter spots a bear very close by to him, but the bear does not see him, so the hunter decides to sneak up on it. He walks 5 km due south then turns to walk 5 km east before turning again to walk 5 km north. To his horror, at the end of his trek he finds himself face to face with the bear, which has not moved an inch.

The question is this: what colour is the bear?

Solution on p. 219

266

Next number

What is the next number in the following sequence?

8643, 3864, 4386, ??

Solution on p. 219

DOTTY

Divide this triangle into four exactly equal areas, each containing the same number of dots.

Solution on p. 219

268 Weather forecast

Cynical Cyril is watching television. At the end of the late night film, the weather forecast comes on. The weatherman says, 'It is raining now and will continue to rain for another two days. However, in 72 hours' time it will be bright and sunny!'

'Wrong again,' snorts Cyril.

How does he know that the forecast is wrong?

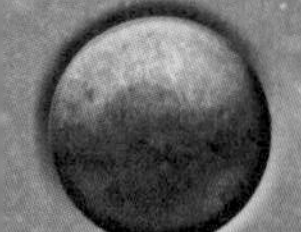

Solution on p. 220

269 DIFFERENT ROOMS

Sylvester walks into a room. He turns around, stands there for a while thinking about this and that, then walks out of the room using the same door he came in through, but this time walking into a different room from the one he had started off in.

How?

Solution on p. 220

270 Three triangles

Move four matches to make one large triangle and two small ones.

Solution on p. 220

271 ANNIVERSARY BLUES

A restaurant runs a deal in which couples are given a free bottle of champagne if it is their wedding anniversary, but they have to bring their certificate to prove it. One Thursday evening, a couple turns up without their certificate and claims their free drinks. The manager is called, and he asks what year they are celebrating. The woman replies that it is their 28th anniversary. The manager asks her to describe her wedding day to him. She effuses, 'It was a wonderful clear Sunday afternoon. Unseasonably warm so we held the reception in the garden ...'

The manager waits to hear the end of the woman's story, then throws the couple out on their ears.

How did he know that she was lying?

Solution on p. 220

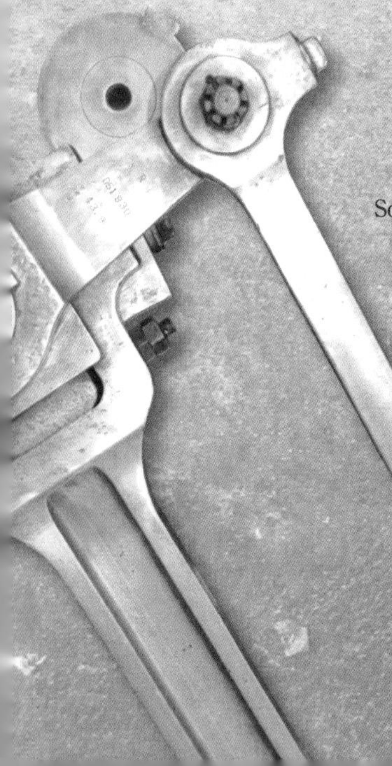

272 Next number

What is the next number in this sequence?

0, 1, 1, 2, 4, 7, 13, 24, 44, ?

Solution on p. 220

273 SCHOOL FETE

Three mothers, June, Claire and Jennifer, are at the annual school fete, where the parents are supposed to bring their own food. June has brought along five dishes and Claire has brought three. An embarrassed Jennifer has nothing. To save Jennifer's blushes, the other two women agree that they should share the dishes equally between them.

Jennifer has 8 pounds on her and offers to pay for what she has eaten by sharing the money between the other two. She suggests paying June 5 pounds and Claire 3 pounds.

This is not a fair deal. Why not?

Solution on p. 220

274 SIX SQUARES

Move three matches to make a figure that contains six squares of the same size.

Solution on p. 220

275 HORSE RACE

Two cowboys have applied for the same job. The ranch manager tells them to ride up to the top of the nearby hill. The one whose horse reaches the summit second will get the job.

The two men jump on a horse and race each other at full gallop to the top of the hill. They both want the job, so why did they do that?

Solution on p. 220

276 HIGH DRAMA

The tightrope walker at Bartram's Circus uses a pole that is 1 metre long to help him to balance. He usually holds the pole with his hands about 60 cm apart, his palms pointing upwards.

One night, when half way along the tightrope, he has a major wobble and the pole slides through his hands so that one end of the pole is now very close to his left hand. Recovering his balance and taking a deep breath, he very carefully slides his hands towards each other at the same speed.

Which way does the pole fall?

Solution on p. 220

277 FOUR SQUARES

Make four identical squares that all touch each other by moving three matches.

Solution on p. 221

278 Missing number

What is the missing number in this series:

???, 130, -1690, 21970, -285610

Solution on p. 221

279 Birthday party

At a child's birthday party there are four mothers, and their children, aged 1, 2, 3 and 4.

It is Juliet's child's birthday party.
Dylan is not the oldest child.
Anne had Holly just over a year ago.
Laura's child will be 3 next birthday.
Graeme is older than Jamie.
Monica's child is the oldest.
Jamie is older than Laura's child.

Whose child is whose, and how old is each child?

Solution on p. 221

280 JOIN THE DOTS

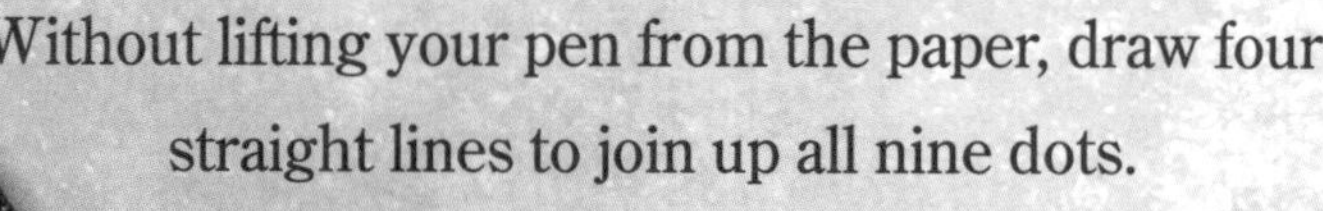

Without lifting your pen from the paper, draw four straight lines to join up all nine dots.

Solution on p. 221

281 Pirates

Captain Blighty's ship is captured by pirates. Before stealing the ship's cargo, the pirates decapitate Captain Blighty and hang his first mate. The rest of the officers lose their head.

The pirates only killed two men. How is this possible?

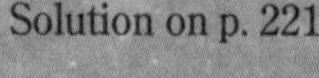

Solution on p. 221

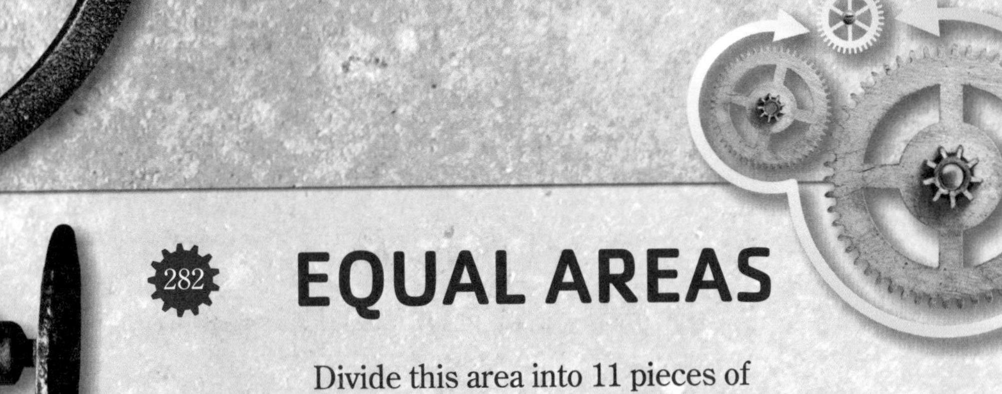

282 EQUAL AREAS

Divide this area into 11 pieces of equal size using 30 matches.

Solution on p. 221

283 COLOUR MAP

What is the fewest number of colours you need to colour in a map of the United States in such a way that no state is touching another state of the same colour?

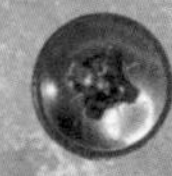

Solution on p. 221

284 THREE SUSPECTS

Three pickpockets are brought into Inspector Crumble's office and made to stand in a line for questioning. Bruce is standing between the clean-shaven man and the man who stole the purse. Crusoe, who stole the wallet, was arrested at the same time as Watson. It was the man with the moustache, not the man with the beard, who stole the watch.

Which man stole which item, and who has what facial hair?

Solution on p. 221

285 HALVING THE SQUARE

Trevor has got his measurements wrong. To make his painting, he needs a square piece of paper 50 cm^2 in size, but he has one that is 100 cm^2. Given that he only wants to paint on one side of the paper, how can Trevor make it the right size given that he doesn't have a ruler or any scissors?

Solution on p. 222

286 Game of chance

A casino runs a game of chance involving bets on the throw of three dice. For a £1 stake, a gambler gets to choose a number from 1 to 6. The dice are then thrown. If their number does not come up on any of the dice, they lose the bet. If their number comes up once, they win £2 (including the stake). If it comes up twice, they win £4, and if it comes up all three times, they win £6.

In the long run, does the house win in this game or do the gamblers win?

Solution on p. 222

287 CROSS INTO A SQUARE

By making just two cuts with a pair of scissors, how would you turn this cross into a square?

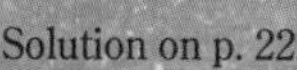
Solution on p. 222

EQUAL AREAS

Using eight matches, divide this shape into four areas the same size and shape.

Solution on p. 222

Replace the letters

Replace the following letters with numerals to make the equation work (each letter represents a different numeral):

ABCD x D = DCBA

Solution on p. 223

290

PHANTOM DOTS

Can you see the grey dots in this figure? Are they ever in the centre of your visual field?

Solution on p. 223

A CLOSE SHAVE?

As he has grown older, James has become very long-sighted. He can no longer focus on anything that is less than 50 cm away. He still enjoys a wet shave every morning, however. How far away from the mirror does James have to be to focus on his face as he shaves?

Solution on p. 223

292 NINE DIAMONDS

Remove four matches to leave nine diamonds.

Solution on p. 223

293 MISSING NUMBER

What is the missing number in this series?

46, 10, 82
29, 11, 47
96, 15, 78
54, 9, 72
42, ??, 15

Solution on p. 223

294 SLIPPING LADDER

Carl has just had a bit of a fright. He was cleaning an upstairs window standing at the top of a 2.5-m ladder. The foot of the ladder was 0.7 m away from the wall at what Carl thought was a safe angle, but the ladder has just slipped, and the top of the ladder where Carl was working has gone down by 0.4 m.

How far has the foot of the ladder moved?

Solution on p. 223

295 What time is it?

Time is really dragging at work for Marjorie. At noon, she looks over at the clock on the wall. The big hand is on the seven, while the little hand is between the four and the five.

What time is it?

Solution on p. 224

296 Seven diamonds

Move four matches to make seven diamonds.

Solution on p. 224

297 Peeling potatoes

Helen has a pile of 55 potatoes in front of her. She begins peeling them at a rate of 2 potatoes per minute. Five minutes later, seeing how slow Helen is working, her mother Grace joins in, peeling at a rate of 5 potatoes per minute. How long does it take them to peel the potatoes, and how many were peeled by each woman? (Once one of them has started on a potato, she has to finish it herself.)

Solution on p. 224

298 What year?

The year 1978 has a special property.
If you add 19 to 78, the result of the sum is
equal to the year's middle two digits, 97.

What will be the next year with this property?
And the year after that one?

Solution on p. 224

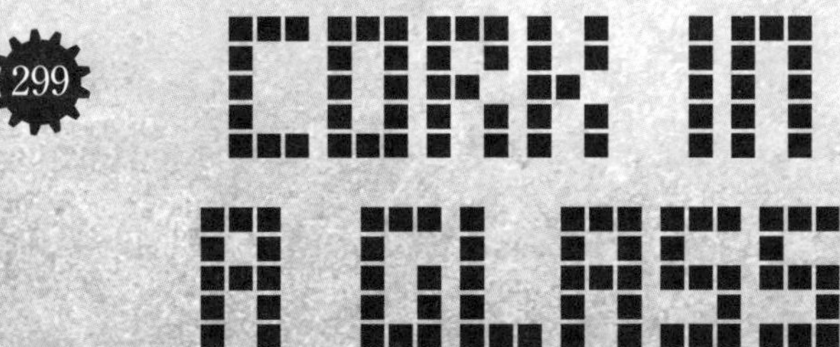

299 CORK IN A GLASS

To make his new magic trick work, Gorky the Clown needs a cork to stay floating in the middle of a glass of water. But try as he might to keep the cork in the centre, it always seems to drift to the edge of the glass.

How would you help Gorky with his new trick?

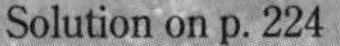

Solution on p. 224

300 Einstein's riddle

And finally, here's a fiendish teaser from Albert Einstein, written at a time when a lot of people smoked!

In a certain street, there are five houses painted five different colours. In each house lives a person of a different nationality. Each person drinks a different kind of beverage, smokes a different brand of cigar and keeps a different kind of pet. We know these 15 facts:

1. The Brit lives in the red house.

2. The Swede keeps dogs as pets.

3. The Dane drinks tea.

4. The green house is on the immediate left of the white house.

5. The green house's owner drinks coffee.

6. The owner who smokes Pall Mall rears birds.

7. The owner of the yellow house smokes Dunhill.

8. The owner living in the centre house drinks milk.

9. The Norwegian lives in the first house.

10. The owner who smokes Blends lives next to the one who keeps cats.

11. The owner who keeps the horse lives next to the one who smokes Dunhill.

12. The owner who smokes Bluemasters drinks beer.

13. The German smokes Prince.

14. The Norwegian lives next to the blue house.

15. The owner who smokes Blends lives next to the one who drinks water.

The question is: Who owns the fish?

Solution on p. 224

ANSWERS

1 He was 12 years old. 29 Feb 1896 was a Saturday, 29 Feb 1904 was a Monday. Remember that the year 1900 was NOT a leap year.

2

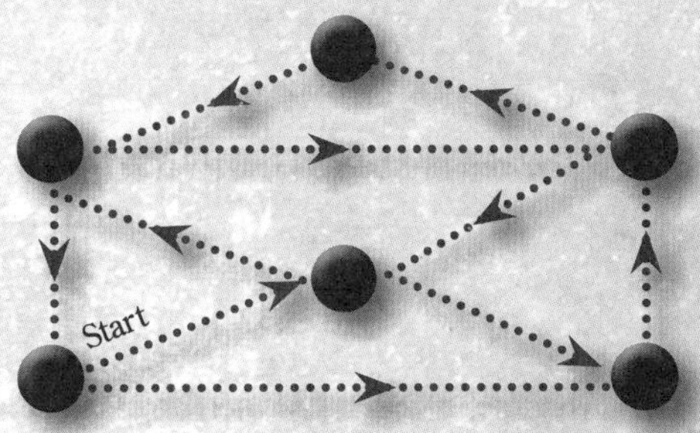

3 First Connie puts the message in the box and locks it with her padlock. She then sends the box to Neville. Neville attaches his padlock to the box and sends it back to Connie with both locks in place. Now, Connie removes her lock and sends the box once again to Neville, this time with just Neville's padlock on it. Neville can now open the box and read Connie's secret message.

4 He travelled 110 km. The next palindrome is 16061 km.

5

6 It is Tuesday.

7. 29. The pattern being followed is: *a*+*b*=*c*, *b*+*c*=*d*, *c*+*d*=*e*, etc.

8.

9. Adam is standing inside his cube.

10.

Do you see the circle?

11. Five rungs are showing. The boat rises with the water level, so the number of rungs showing is unchanged.

12. He was 84.

If you call his total life x, you can make the following equation:

$\frac{1}{6}x + \frac{1}{12}x + \frac{1}{7}x + 5 + \frac{1}{2}x + 4 = x$

The solution to the equation is 84.

13 It cannot. The train has already taken 2 hours to cover the first half of the journey. However fast it goes from now on, it's going to be late!

14 68782 + 68782 + 650 = 138214

15 Elizabeth and Hannah play all three instruments. James plays none of them.

16

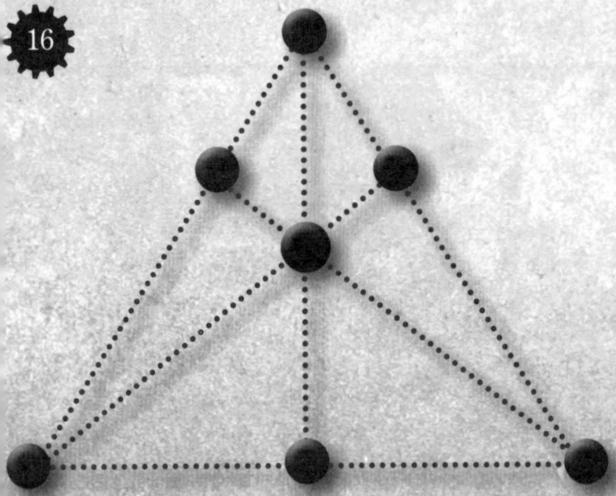

17 She makes a fruit salad!

18

19 There are three different colours, so he must take out at least four socks to be sure of a matching pair.

20 Zero. One of the terms is $(x - x)$, which is 0, and any number multiplied by zero is zero.

21 It takes 8 days. It starts the 8th day at 7 metres up, and reaches the top at nightfall on that day.

22 There are 30 rectangles in total. (Remember that squares are a kind of rectangle.)

23 Just the one. After that, the glass is no longer empty!

24

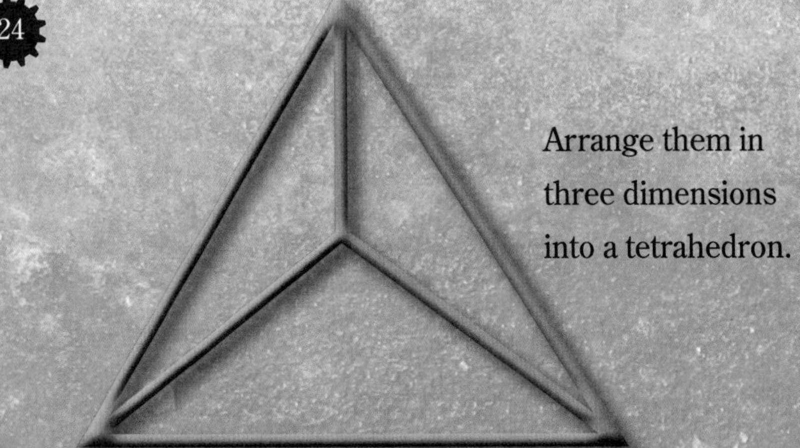

Arrange them in three dimensions into a tetrahedron.

25 There are 54 games. Each game results in one player leaving the tournament, so for *n* competitors, there will be (*n* - 1) games.

26 She can score 100 using six arrows:

17 + 17 + 17 + 17 +16 + 16 = 100

27 The contestant should switch. She stands a ⅓ chance of winning if she sticks to her original choice, but a ⅔ chance if she switches. To see how this must be, think of it this way: When she made her original choice, there was a ⅓ chance that the car was behind door 1. Being told that behind one of the other doors is a goat does not change these odds – she already knew that. At the time of making the original choice, the odds that the car is behind either door 2 or door 3 are ⅔. After being shown the goat, she now knows that it is not door 3, so now the odds that it is door 2 are ⅔.

28 The same: £1,224.45 per year.

29

30 27 + 56 = 83

40 + 16 = 56

93 + 16 = 109

31

32

13112221

Reading what you see, the series is 'One 1', 'Two 1', One 2, Two 1', etc.

33

For each round of picking up sticks, Alexander must make sure that the number adds up to four. So if Graham picks up one stick, Alexander picks up three. If Graham picks up two sticks, Alexander also picks up two. If Graham picks up three, Alexander picks up one. By doing this, Alexander is ensuring that after five rounds, 20 sticks will have been picked up, leaving 1 stick left, which Graham must pick up.

34

35

If he tosses the coin twice, he knows that, whatever the bias, HT (heads then tails) is as likely as TH. So he tosses it twice. If it comes up HT he goes to the pub. If it comes up TH, he stays in. If it comes up HH or TT, he tosses the coin twice more. And so on until he gets either HT or TH.

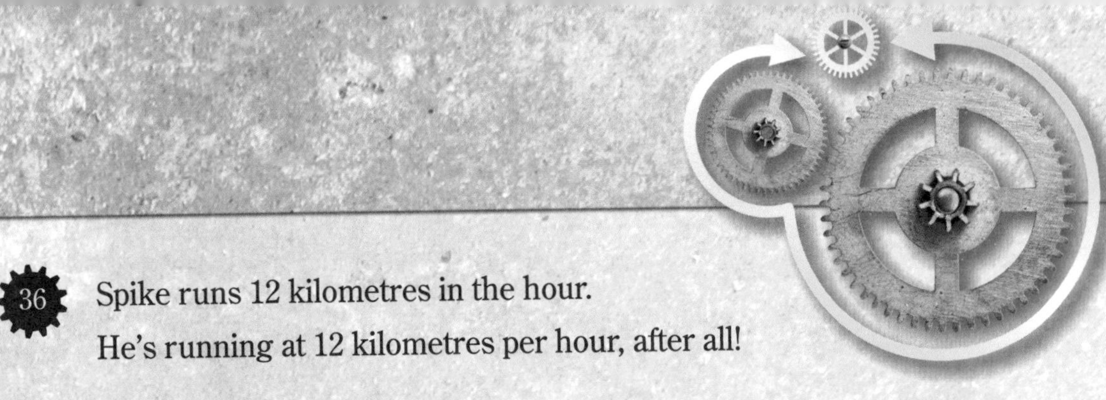

36 Spike runs 12 kilometres in the hour.
He's running at 12 kilometres per hour, after all!

37 10. The pattern here is alternately adding 3 and then subtracting 2.

38 They are both the same length!

39 There are 7 sea lions on the larger rock and 5 on the smaller rock. You can work this out by making the following equations, where a is the larger group and b is the smaller group:

$a + 1 = 2(b - 1)$

$a - 1 = b + 1$

40 It would take him 24 days. In 8 days, Geoffrey can mow ⅔ of the lawns, so Lewis mows ⅓ of the lawns in 8 days. This means that Lewis could mow all the lawns in 3 x 8 days.

41

42

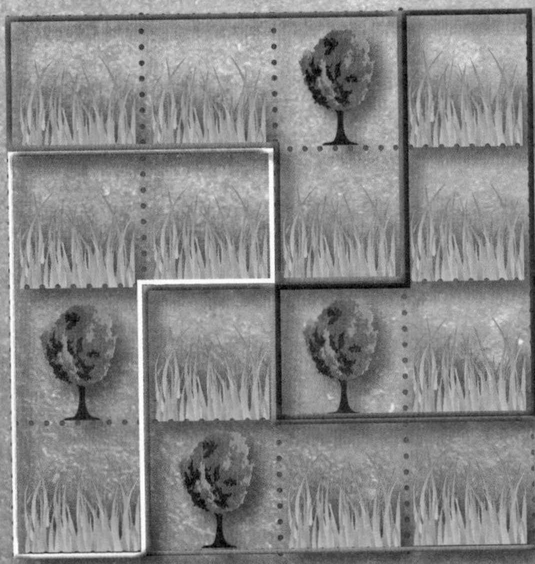

43

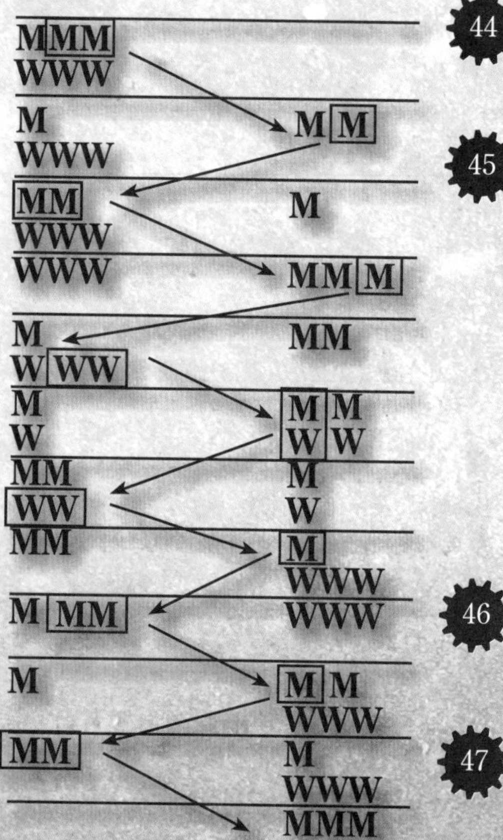

44 The grandmother she is talking about is her father's mother.

45 They are exactly the same shade of grey! We are fooled into thinking that there is a shadow on a regular board of white and grey squares, so we compensate accordingly. To see that this is really true, try covering up the other squares.

46 Once, as it is the same size as the first gear.

47 Anticlockwise. The first, third and fifth gears will turn clockwise, and the second and fourth gears will turn anticlockwise.

48 The sister on the left cannot be Anne, as that would make Anne a liar. The sister in the middle cannot be Anne either, for the same reason. So the sister on the right must be Anne. Anne tells the truth, so the sister in the middle is Beatrix. That makes the sister on the left Caroline.

49

50 He crosses his arms before taking hold of the rope. When he uncrosses his arms, he will make a knot in the rope.

51 82 cm. As the books stand in the shelf, page 1 of Volume 1 and the last page of Volume 10 are not at the end of the stack!

52 When he takes the marble out of the bag, Gordon should cover it with his hand, put it straight into his mouth and swallow it. The Inner Circle will then look at the other marble, see that it is black, and conclude that Gordon has swallowed the white marble. Lord Sleight will have to accept the decision or he would be exposed as a cheat!

53 $11^3 = 1331$

54 Mrs Thomas's garden is three times the size of Mrs Brown's garden.

55 Did you spot the mistake? If not, turn back and read it again.

56 He is buying the brass numbers for his front door.

57

58 Let the distance AC, the radius of the larger circle, be x. CD = x - 9 and EC = x - 5. x - 5 is the mean proportional between the points x - 9 and x, a property derived from similar triangles. This means that $(x - 9)/(x - 5) = (x - 5)/x$, therefore $x = 25$. So the larger circle has a diameter of 50 cm, and the smaller circle has a diameter of 41 cm.

59 The four drinkers are a man and his sister plus his daughter and her son (or her daughter and his son).

60 The 30 cm pizza is better value. You're getting 225π cm^2 of pizza for £10. With the special offer, you get 200π cm^2 for £10.50 – less pizza for more dough!

61

62 He starts both timers running at the same time. When the 4-minute timer runs out, he turns it over straight away. When the 7-minute one runs out, he turns that over straight away, too. Then when the 4-minute timer runs out for the second time, meaning 8 minutes are up, he turns the 7-minute timer over. This timer has only been running for one minute, so when it runs out again, 9 minutes are up.

63

64 He is 120 cm tall.

65 First the farmer pours the lentils into the brewer's sack. He then binds the sack tightly and turns it inside out. Next, he pours the grain into the sack. Finally, he unbinds the sack and pours the lentils back into his own sack.

66 $\frac{7}{12}$. 58$\frac{1}{3}$ per cent is 58$\frac{1}{3}$/100. Multiply both sides by 3 and you get 175/300, which is 7/12.

67

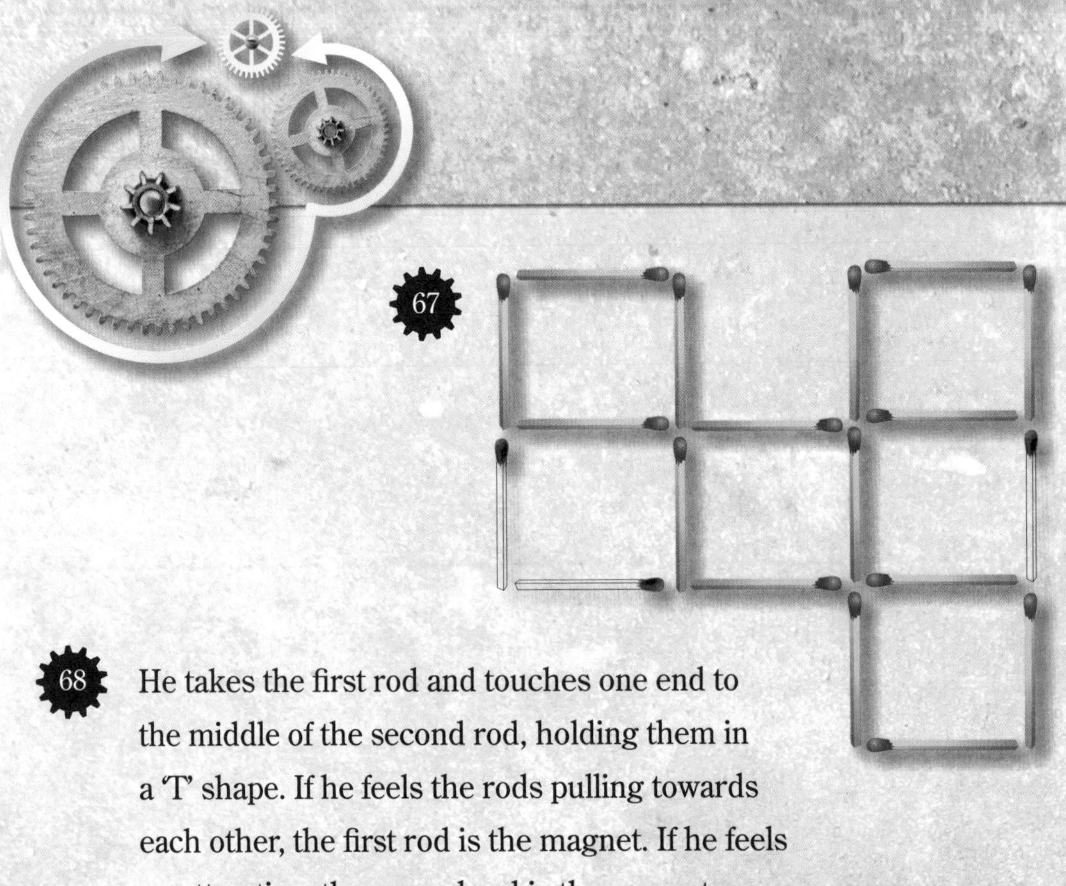

68 He takes the first rod and touches one end to the middle of the second rod, holding them in a 'T' shape. If he feels the rods pulling towards each other, the first rod is the magnet. If he feels no attraction, the second rod is the magnet. This works because the centre of a magnet does not pull iron objects towards it, but both ends of a magnet – its North and South poles – do.

69 5050. The sum can be expressed in 50 pairs, all of which add up to 101: (100 + 1), (99 + 2) ... (51 + 50). So the sum is the product of 50 x 101 = 5050

70 It is 5 paces across. The two distances he has walked form the shorter sides of a right-angled triangle. The diameter is the hypotenuse of the triangle. As we know from Pythagoras, its square is equal to the squares of the other two sides: $3^2 + 4^2 = 5^2$

71

72 None. It's a hole!

73 The minimum number of goes needed is four. Here are the four turns you need to make: RBG, RGY, RBY, BGY. You've now turned each card three times, so they are all upside-down. This will work whichever order you carry out the four turns in.

74 7. Each entry is the square of the previous entry.

75 The key fact to remember is that he can safely leave the wolf alone with the grain. First, he crosses the river with the goat. He leaves the goat on its own and comes back. Next trip, he takes the wolf across, but comes back with the goat. Now he takes the grain across, leaving the goat on its own again. Leaving the wolf with the grain on the far side of the river, he finally returns to pick up the goat.

76

77 20 times.

78 Yes, once. To see this, imagine two climbers each setting off at the same time on the same day. They will have to pass each other somewhere along the route, no matter what speed they are going at.

79 They are parallel!

80 The house is at the South Pole.

81 The wallaby will win. It completes the race in 100 hops. The kangaroo needs 68 hops to complete the race as its 34th hop will take it 2 metres past the pole. At the moment the wallaby reaches the finishing line, the kangaroo will be in midair as it takes its 67th hop.

82 He needs to cut the wood into three pieces. Numbering the corners as below, first he measures the mid-point between B and C, which we will call A. He then draws lines from A to E and A to D and cuts along those lines, placing the pieces back together as shown.

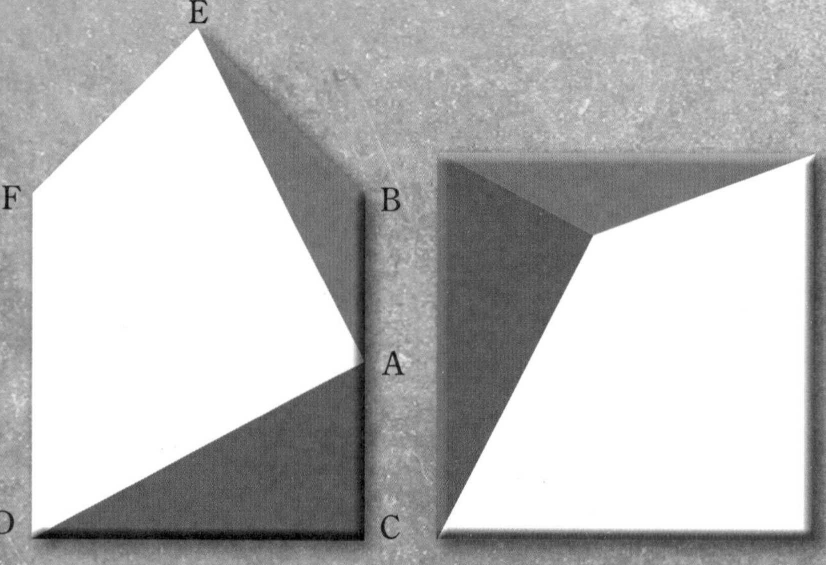

83 There are 31 squares.

84 The original order was 3, 5, 4, 2, as seen from Geraldine's perspective.

85

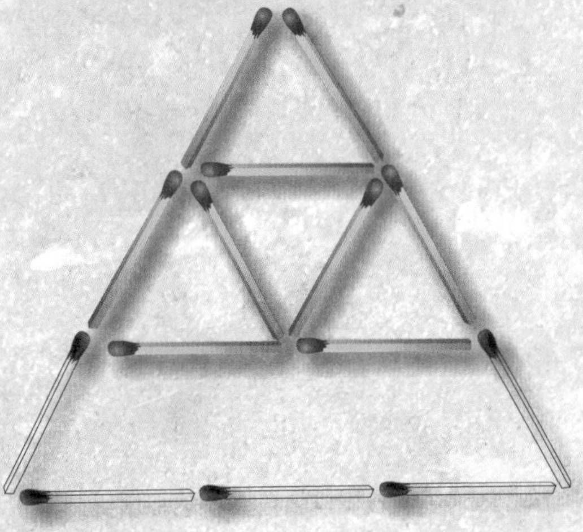

86 Elijah is Patrick's grandfather.

87 There are several possible combinations, but they all take at least four goes. For instance, you could change row 2, then column A, then column D, then row 4.

88

The trick is to view this as a 3D image in perspective. Then the scales balance!

89 First fold the paper into a concertina shape. The paper will then take the book's weight without crumpling.

90

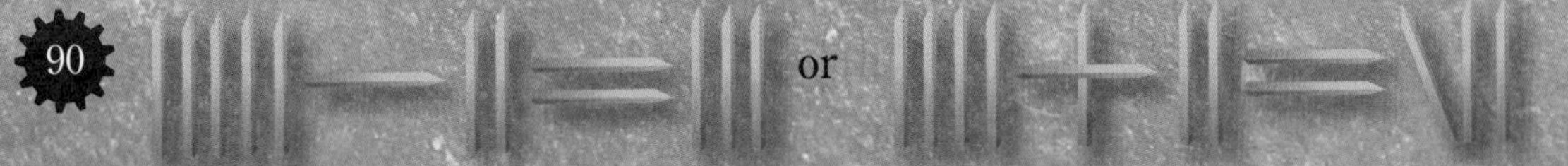

91 None! As Mr Trubshaw knows all too well, his mill has closed down.

92 

93 It weighs 1 kg.

94 545+5=550

95 It was the middle of the day.
Nobody said anything about night-time!

96 They are onto a sure-fire winner! They may not be able to see their own hats, but they can see each other's. One guesses that his hat is the same colour as the other's: if he sees black, he guesses black. The other guesses that his hat is a different colour: if he sees black, he guesses red. Their hats must be either the same colour or different colours, so one of them – and only one – is guaranteed to be right.

97

98 They are both the same distance from Abigail's house when they meet!

99 2999. Divide 29 by 9, and that's how many 9s there are in the number. The remainder, 2, comes first.

100 There are two: a duck and a rabbit. But keep staring at it. Can you see both the duck and the rabbit at the same time, or do you only ever see one or the other?

101 There were 11 people at the party. The first person toasts with 10 others, the second 9, etc., so the total number of clinks is 10 + 9 + 8 + 7 + 6 + 5 + 4 + 3 + 2 + 1 = 55

102 He is lying. Bill's statement cannot be true because if it were, he would have told a truth, which contradicts the statement. It must be the case that he sometimes – but not always – lies, and that he is lying on this occasion.

103 The rectangle has an area of 2 units. The square needs an area of 2 units, too. This means that the square has sides that are √2 long. Slicing the rectangle into four triangles with a hypotenuse of √2 does the trick.

104 This time the area of the rectangle is 5 units, so the square needs sides that are √5. Four triangles with sides of 1, 2 and √5 can be made, plus a small square for them to fit around.

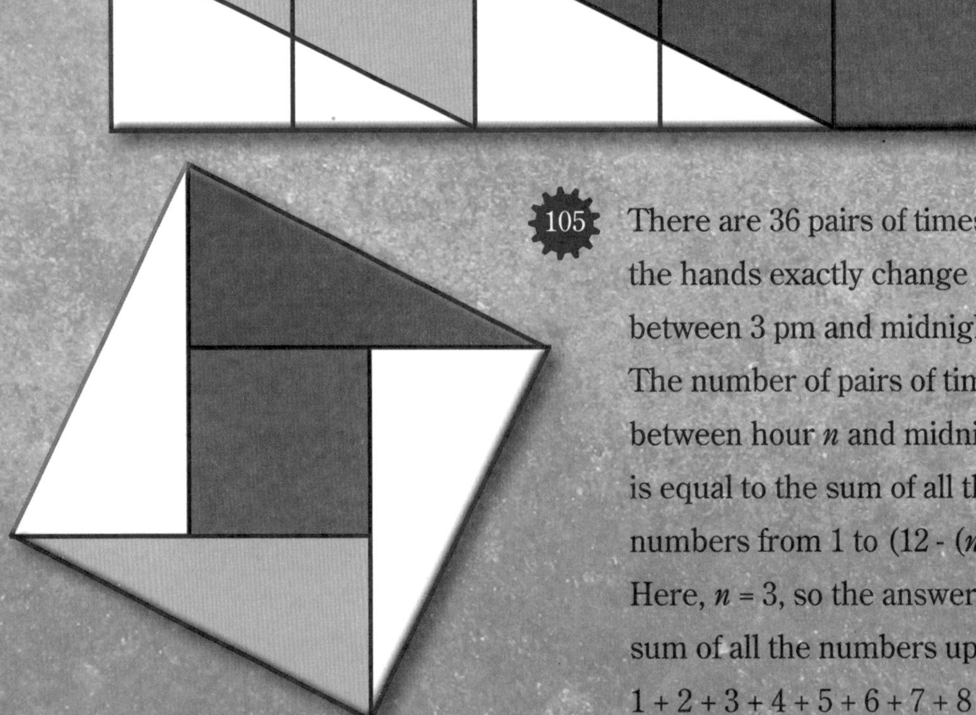

105 There are 36 pairs of times when the hands exactly change places between 3 pm and midnight. The number of pairs of times between hour n and midnight is equal to the sum of all the numbers from 1 to $(12 - (n + 1))$. Here, $n = 3$, so the answer is the sum of all the numbers up to 8: $1 + 2 + 3 + 4 + 5 + 6 + 7 + 8 = 36$

In this case, half of 13 is 8. Write out the numbers in Roman numerals, then chop them in half!

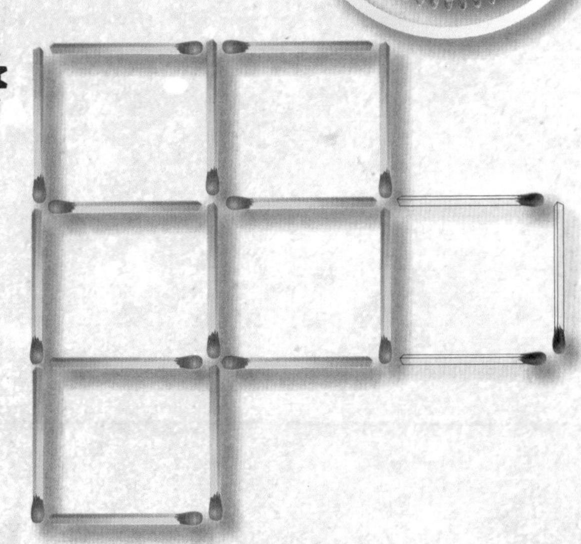

He will need 8 bags, containing the following amounts:

1, 2, 4, 8, 16, 32, 64, 12

To work this out, you need the series $2^0 + 2^1 + 2^2 ... + 2^6$, which gives a total of 127. With those you can make any number up to 127. Add the bag of 12, and you can make any number up to 139.

$1 + 2 + 3 + 4 + 5 + 6 + 7 + (8 \times 9) = 100$

She has 3 chickens and 6 pigs.

To work this out, make x the number of chickens, y the number of pigs.

$x + y = 9$; $2x + 4y = 30$ Solving the equations, $y = 6$, $x = 3$

The water level goes down. While the anchor is in the boat, it displaces an amount of water equal to its weight. When it is dropped overboard, the anchor only displaces an amount of water equal to its volume.

112

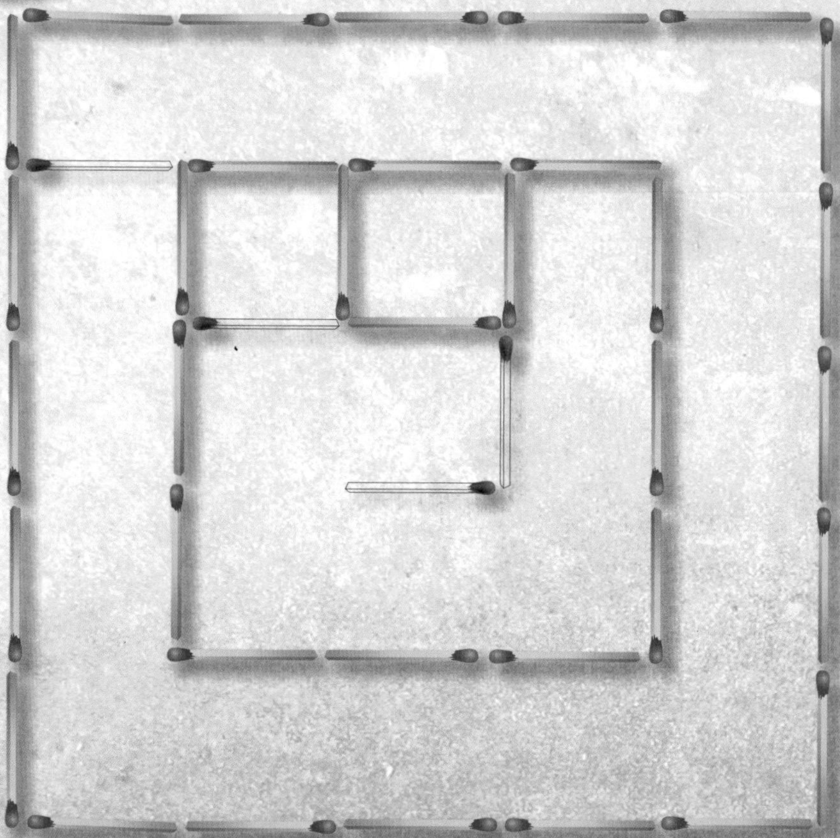

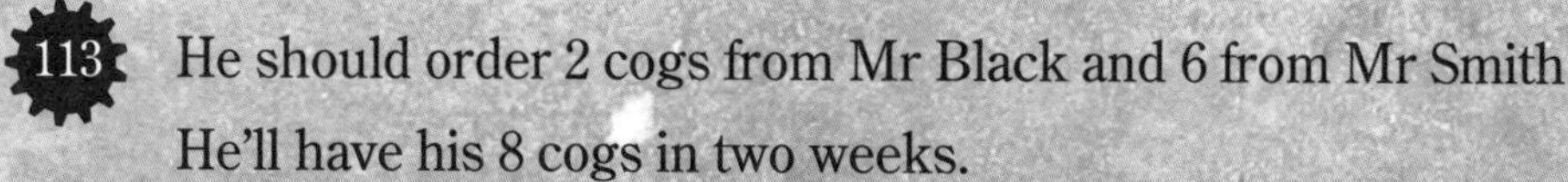

113 He should order 2 cogs from Mr Black and 6 from Mr Smith. He'll have his 8 cogs in two weeks.

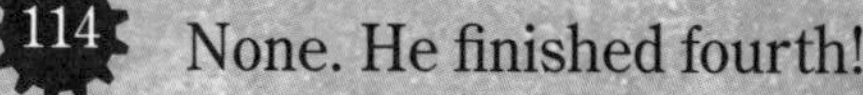

114 None. He finished fourth!

115 Not 35 minutes! If she can ride 12 km in 30 minutes with the wind, she can ride 16 km in 40 minutes with the wind. Against the wind, she manages 12 km in 40 minutes. So her speed without any wind would be 14 km in 40 minutes. She only needs to cycle 12 km, so it takes her $12 \times {}^{40}/_{14}$ minutes, which is 34 minutes, 28 $^{2}/_{7}$ seconds.

116 She lights one wick at one end, and at the same time lights the other wick at both ends. When the second wick has burned all the way down, she knows that half an hour has passed. At that moment, she lights the other end of the second wick. When this second wick has burned down, she knows that 45 minutes will have passed.

They weren't playing each other!

If she sells the lot, Mrs Smith will get 24 pence. She will give Mrs Bramley 15 pence for her apples, leaving Mrs Smith with 9 pence. But Mrs Smith's 30 apples were worth 10 pence to her, so she's diddled herself out of a penny.

$5^7 = 78125$

1 kg, 3 kg, 9 kg and 27 kg

He can put the weights on either side of the balance:

1kg = 1 kg; 2 kg = 3 kg – 1 kg; 3 kg = 3 kg ...

39kg = 27kg + 9kg + 3kg; 40kg = 27kg + 9kg + 3kg + 1kg

122 200 cm. If you rolled out the cylinder into a flat rectangle, it would look like this. The line traces the path of four diagonal lines. Each line is the hypotenuse of a right-angled triangle with one side 40 cm and the other 30 cm (120 ÷ 4). Using Pythagoras' theorem, we see that the line is 4 x 50 cm = 200 cm long

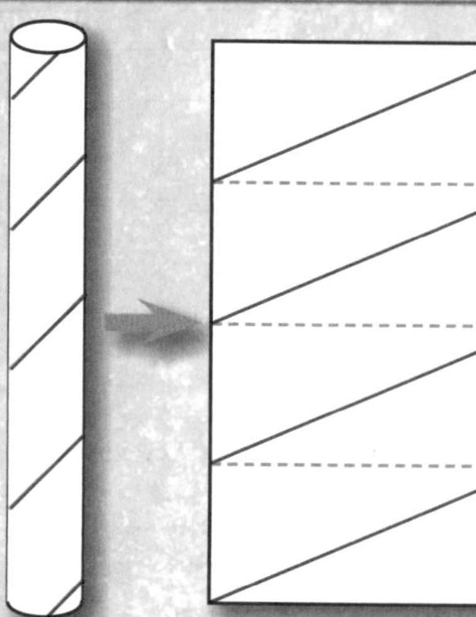

123 135 = (1 + 3 + 5) x 1 x 3 x 5

124 First she turns two switches to the 'on' position and leaves them there for five minutes. Then she turns one of these two switches off and goes downstairs. She knows that the bulb that is on is controlled by the switch that is on. She feels the other two bulbs. The bulb that is warm is controlled by the switch she turned on and then off again. The bulb that is cold is controlled by the switch that she has not turned on at all.

125 They must both be lying. If only one had been lying, they would both have said that they were boys or both have said that they were girls. So you know that the child with blue eyes is the girl and the child with brown eyes is the boy.

126

127 The prisoner said: 'I will face the firing squad.' The king could not deem the statement true or false. If he deems it true, it cannot come true. If he deems it false, it must come true. Bewildered, the king gives the prisoner a pardon.

128 888 + 88 + 8 + 8 + 8 = 1000

129 They are a 9-year-old and two twins aged 2. As their product is 36, they could only be aged 9, 2 and 2 or 6, 6 and 1. Upon finding out that there is an eldest, the census taker knows that they must be 9, 2 and 2.

130 A decimal point. It gives you 4.9.

131 We know that Mr Blue must be wearing either a black or red shirt. But the man in the black shirt replied to the first man, calling him Mr Blue. This means that Mr Blue must be in the red shirt. The man in the black shirt can only be Mr Blue or Mr Red, but Mr Blue is in the red shirt, so we know that the man in the black shirt must be Mr Red. This leaves the man who didn't speak as Mr Black sporting a blue shirt.

132 The carpenter uses 96 nails. Each corner needs one nail, then each side has 23 more.

133

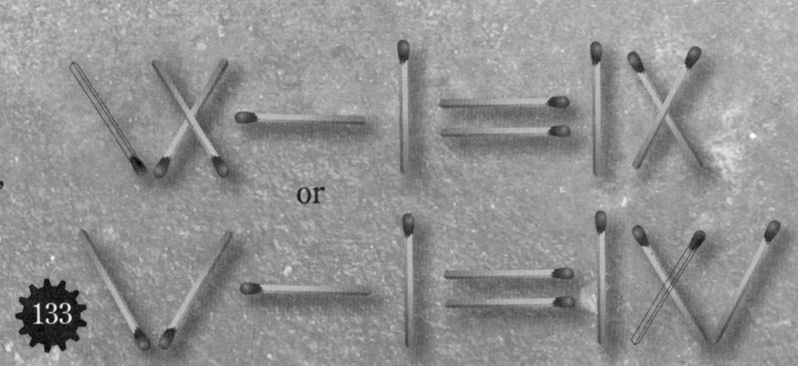

134 There are eight teams in the League. If they played each other only once, the first team would play 7 other teams, the second 6, etc. So the total would be 7 + 6 + 5 + 4 + 3 + 2 + 1 = 28
However, they play each other twice, so 28 x 2 = 56

135 He should ask: 'Which door would the other guard tell me was the door to freedom?'
He then chooses the other door.

136 The total is 4100. Did you make it 5000? Don't worry, most people do.

137 Edward!

138 First he fills flask A with blood from flask C. Then he pours the contents of flask A into flask B. Next, he fills flask A again with blood from flask C. He fills flask B from flask A and pours away what is left in flask A. Now he fills flask A from flask B. This leaves 2 litres in flask B and 2 litres in flask C. Pouring the contents of flask B into flask C gives him his 4 litres.

139

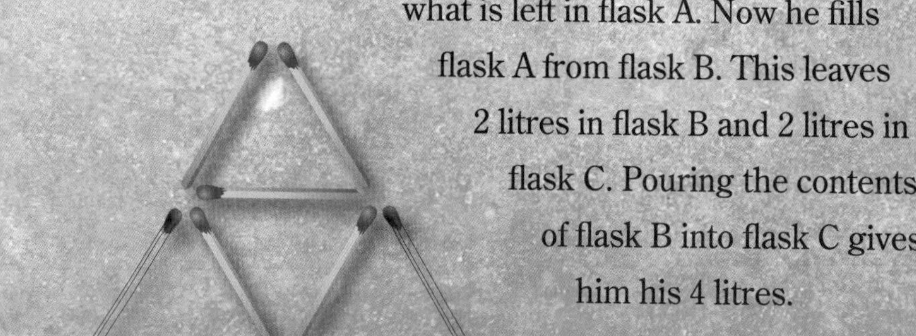

He takes a piece of wood and lights it on the fire. He then returns to a point a few metres in from the east end of the island and starts a fire there. This new fire will burn across right to the east coast, and the man can take shelter in the area it burns out. What he does for food after the fire has burnt out is another question!

60 metres.

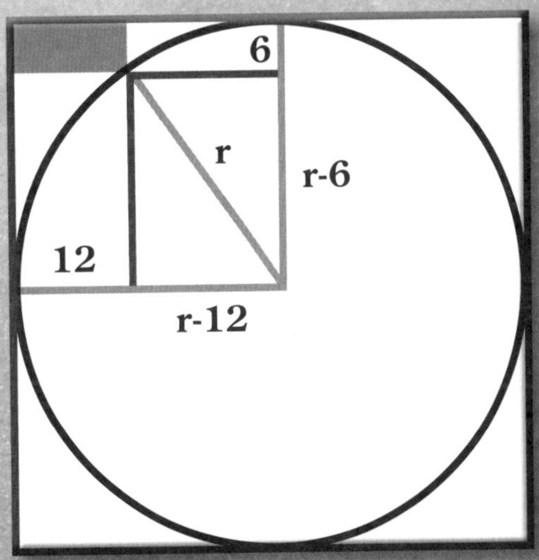

To find the radius, you need to make a right-angled triangle with the radius as the hypotenuse. So, using Pythagoras' theorem, $(r - 6)^2 + (r - 12)^2 = r^2$. This simplifies to: $r^2 - 36r + 180 = 0$. On factorizing, we get: $(r - 30)(r - 6) = 0$; so: $r = 30$ or 6. However, we can reject the solution $r = 6$ as this would give a negative length $(r - 12)$. So, $r = 30$, the diameter $= 2 \times 30 = 60$

She gives 23 of the children a sweet, and gives the 24th child the tin with the last sweet still in it.

34. Each term is the sum of the two previous terms. This is known as the Fibonacci series, and it crops up a lot in nature.

The figure of the girl at the front is the largest. The perspective lines fool us into thinking that the top figure is larger because we perceive it to be further away.

Look carefully at the large figures. The red and blue triangles have different slopes, so neither of the large figures is a triangle. The bottom figure in fact bulges up slightly along the red–blue side, while the top figure sinks in slightly. This is how area A appears.

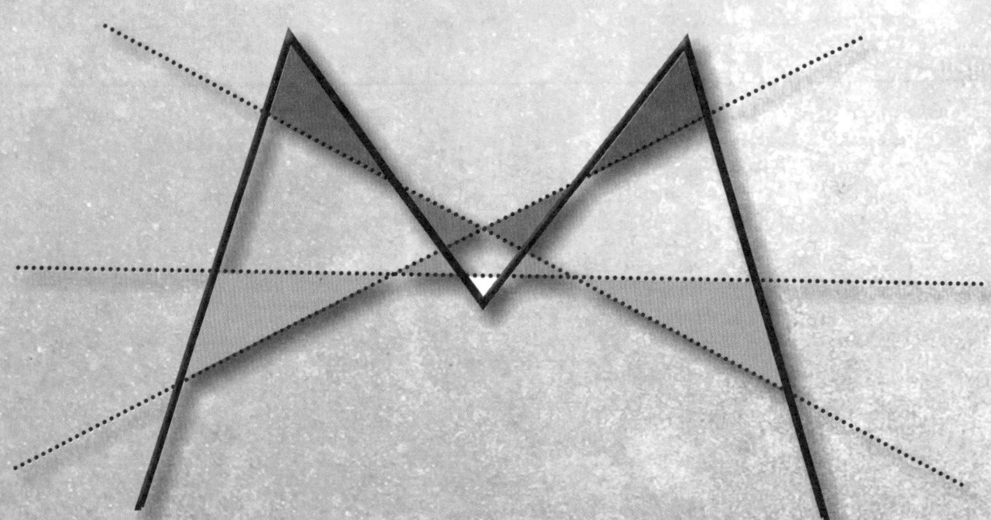

He must break the chocolate 31 times. There are 32 squares. He starts off with one piece, and each time he breaks a piece, he increases the number of pieces he has by one, so he must break the chocolate (32 - 1) times to get 32 separate pieces.

You need just 6.28 metres more rope. The radius of the circle has been increased by 1 metre. The circumference of a circle is $2\pi r$. So the extra rope you need is 2π metres, or approximately 6.28.

5 pounds.

9567 + 1085 = 10652

They are both perfectly round!

In one hour, the pool gets $\frac{5}{60} + \frac{12}{60} + \frac{6}{60} + \frac{10}{60}$ full, which equals $\frac{33}{60}$. It will be completely full in $\frac{60}{33}$ hours = 1 hour, 49 minutes and 6 $\frac{2}{3}$ seconds.

156 She bought 18 eggs. The grocer offered her 16 for 12 pence and threw in 2 extra. The original offer would have been 9 pence a dozen. The second offer was 8 pence a dozen.

157 9 marbles. Top scale shows:
shell (s) + 3 cubes (c) = 12 marbles (m), so $c = 4m - \frac{1}{3}s$
Substituting into the middle scale, we see that $4s/3 = 12m$

158 15 minutes. Relative to the carriage, he is driving at 8 km/h. When he stops, it will be catching him up at 8 km/h, or 2 km per 15 minutes, so he needs to drive long enough to get ahead by 2 km, which is 15 minutes.

159 They are both married, but not to each other!

160 Opinions vary about this paradox, but here is one way to look at it. As Euthalus has not yet won a case, the court will necessarily have to rule against Protagoras, so Euthalus will not have to pay. However, if Protagoras were to bring another case, he would surely win that case, and Euthalus would have to pay up. Alternatively, Euthalus could get another lawyer to represent him in court!

161

162 His father!

163 The most likely result is an approximation to π (pi), which is roughly 3.14!

164 Andrea is 20 years old. Her mother is 40.
Ten years ago, Andrea was 10, and her mother was 30.

165

166 He seats the clerks back-to-back.

167 There is no missing pound. The travellers spent £27 in the end, not £30. Of that £27, £25 went to the hotel, and £2 to the bellboy.

168 The cabin is the cabin of a plane.
The men died in a plane crash.

169 By the time the lorry has driven the 5 km to the centre of the bridge, it has burned more than 500 g in weight of fuel, so even with the pigeon on it, it is still under the 20-tonne limit.

170 The chances that both the children were girls are ½, or 50:50. Calling the children child 1 and child 2, there are four possibilities (child 1 comes first): GG, GB, BG and BB. After finding out that one is a girl, clearly, BB is impossible. If child 1 is the girl we know about, then only possibilities GB and GG are possible. If child 2 is the girl we know about, only possibilities BG and GG are possible. In both cases, there is a 50:50 chance of GG.

171

172 You don't bury survivors!

173 He picks up the second glass, pours its contents into the fifth glass, then places the second glass back where it was.

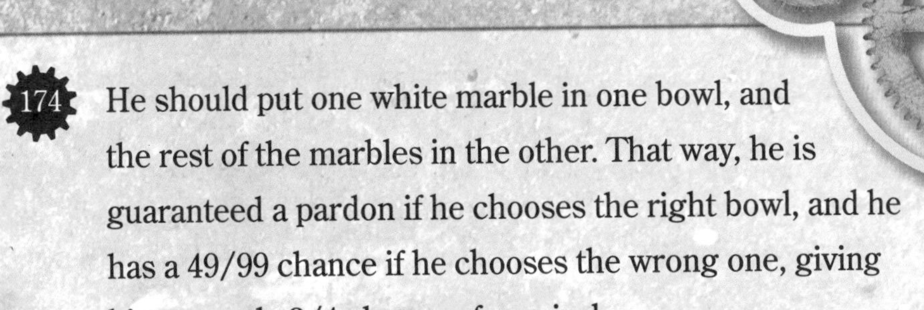

174 He should put one white marble in one bowl, and the rest of the marbles in the other. That way, he is guaranteed a pardon if he chooses the right bowl, and he has a 49/99 chance if he chooses the wrong one, giving him a nearly 3/4 chance of survival.

175 There are two possible solutions:

5795 + 6435 + 2505 = 14735 or 5305 + 2475 + 6595 = 14375

176 There were just three men: a man, his father and his grandfather.

177

178 2 minutes. When the front of the train enters the tunnel, the back is 1 km away, so the train needs to travel 2 km until the back of the train reaches the end of the tunnel. The train is travelling at 1 km per minute, so it takes 2 minutes to pass through the tunnel.

179 You need to turn over the 8 and the brown card. You are only testing whether or not even cards are red. The red card could be even or odd without disproving the statement. This test was devised by psychologist Peter Cathcart Wason. Most people get it wrong!

180 They tip the cask over so that the wine level reaches the brim. If they can see the bottom of the cask, Dee the pessimist has got it right. If not, Dum the optimist is correct.

181 First he numbers the tins 1 to 12. He takes one pill from tin 1, two from tin 2, three from tin 3, up to 12 from tin 12. He now has 78 pills in total. If all the pills are aspirin, they will weigh 780 g. If tin 1 is arsenic, then one of the pills will be arsenic, and they will weigh 779 g. If tin 2 is arsenic, they will weigh 778 g, etc. So by subtracting the reading on the scales from 780, he will arrive at the number of the tin containing the arsenic.

182 The ladder has 23 rungs.

183 13 x 4 = 52

184

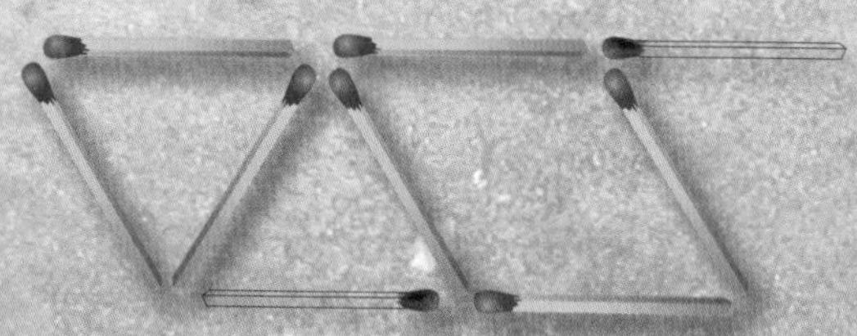

185 2 hours 15 minutes.

186 Two. Only Mrs Tyler was going to the market!

187 The case is a rectangle 120 cm long and 90 cm wide. It has an outside diagonal 150 cm long, and an inside diagonal a little bit shorter than that (allowing for the width of the wood). So it can carry a cue that is nearly 150 cm long.

188 40

189 Still 40. There are 13 different kinds of card in each suit, so the slowest way to draw 4 of a kind is (13 x 3) + 1. This is true however many decks of cards you are drawing from.

190 They are both the same size!

191 There are two possible solutions:
5832/17496 or 5823/17469

192 She breaks all the links in one of the short chains and uses them to link the other three together. That way, she only has to break three links.

193 60°. Imagine a third line as shown on the right. The three lines now make an equilateral triangle, which has three internal angles of 60°.

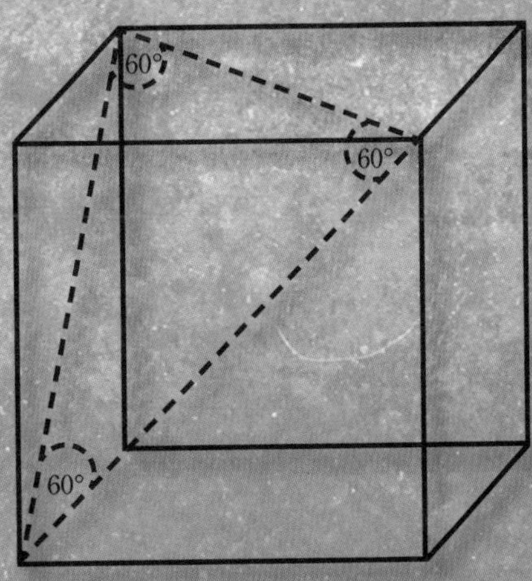

194

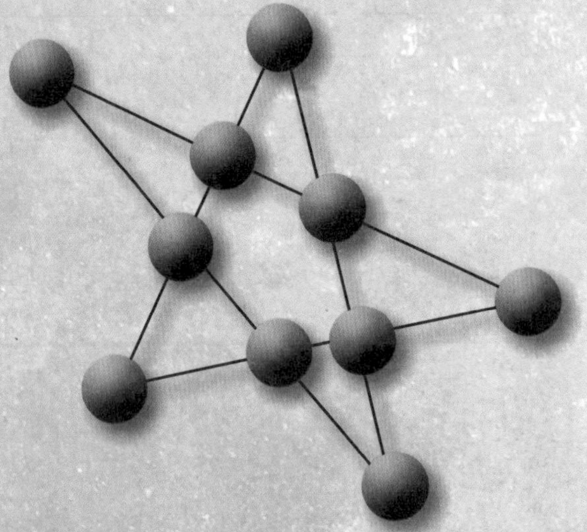

195 He puts one of the diamonds in the small box, then puts the small box and the other two diamonds in the big box. Alternatively, he puts all three diamonds in the small box then puts it in the big box.

196 (5 x 5 x 5) - (5 x 5) = 100

197 Roger is 40. Matthew is four and Theresa is one.

198 It is 9 pm.

199 By turning the book upside-down!
X = I + IX

200 You need to make 6 slices. Each slice reveals one face of the small cube at the centre of the larger cube. Once all six of its faces have been revealed, all 27 cubes will have been separated.

201 As all the labels are wrong, the box labelled 'gold or silver' must be the box containing the bronze coins. Therefore, the box labelled silver must contain the gold, and the box labelled gold must contain the silver.

202

203 10 pence and 20 pence.
Only one of the coins is not a 10-pence piece, remember.

204 Do you see the circles rotate?

205 The carpet should be cut like this:

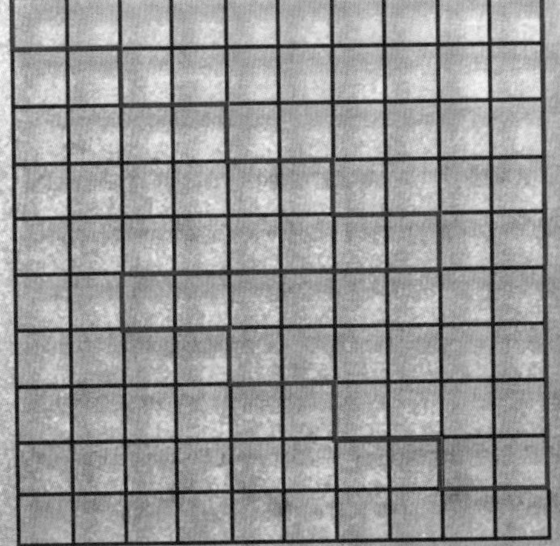

It will fit the room like this:

206 80. 30 divided by ½ equals 60.

207 They average exactly one pen each, so they have 360 pens between them.

208 Three. She has lost two – her sight and her hearing.

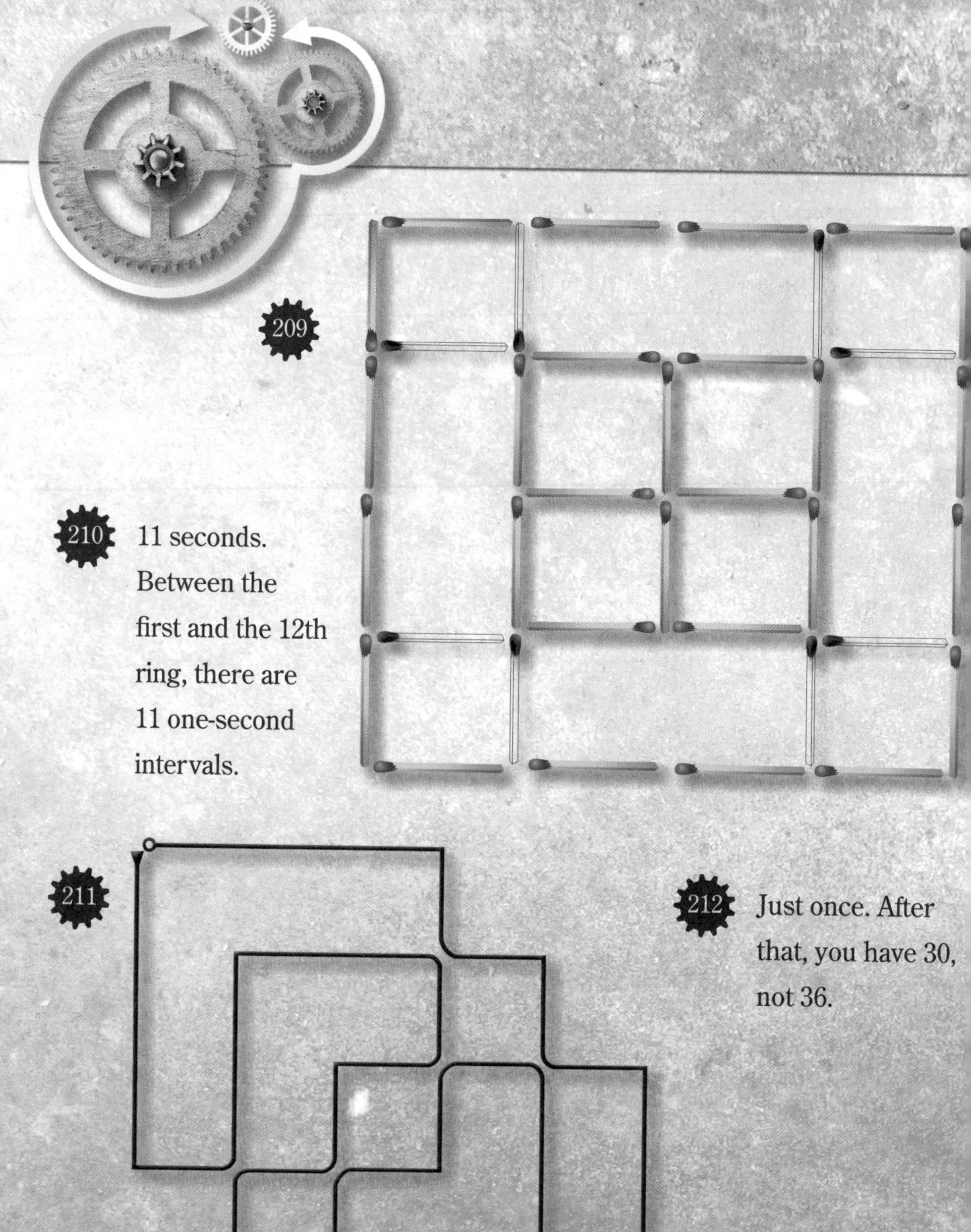

209

210 11 seconds. Between the first and the 12th ring, there are 11 one-second intervals.

211

212 Just once. After that, you have 30, not 36.

If you are right-handed, you probably think the bottom figure is the happier. If you are left-handed, the top figure is likely to appear more jolly. This test was devised by psychologist Julian Jaynes to show how our perception is affected by the left–right lateralization of our brains.

50 eggs. In eight days, 200 hens would lay on average 200 eggs, so in two days, they will lay a quarter of that number.

His horse is called Friday!

William has earned £3.25 in all. He made £2.25 in the first week, £0.75 in the second week and only £0.25 in the third week.

At first, it probably looks as though the stairs lead up from right to left. But keep looking, and you will see an upside-down staircase, too. You cannot see both at the same time, however, and you should feel a distinct shift every time your brain switches from one interpretation of the image to the other. Do you see it switch when you blink?

(1 + 9 + 6 + 8 + 3) x (1 + 9 + 6 + 8 + 3) x (1 + 9 + 6 + 8 + 3) = 19683

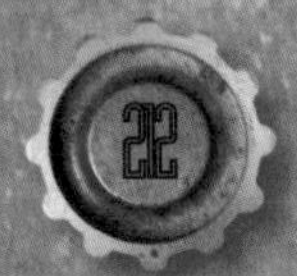

220 First he made a fold in the paper as shown by the dotted line. Taking points A and B, he drew semi-circles alternately taking B then A then B then A as the centre, being careful to make the ends join each time.

221 Cycling may be his profession, but on this particular day, he was driving his car!

222

223 It will take him at least six minutes. If you call the cakes A, B and C, he bakes A and B on side 1, then A on side 2 and C on side 1, then finally B and C on side 2.

224

First he splits the stones into three groups of 27. He weighs two of the groups against each other. If one group is heavier than the other, he knows that the fake is in that group. If the two groups are balanced, he knows that the fake is in the group he did not weigh. Now he takes the group of 27 that contains the fake, splits it into three groups of nine and repeats the process for the second weighing. He takes the resultant group of nine and splits it into three groups of three for the third weighing. After three weighings, he has three stones left for his final weighing. He weighs two of them against each other. If one is heavier, that is the fake. If they are balanced, the stone he has not weighed is the fake.

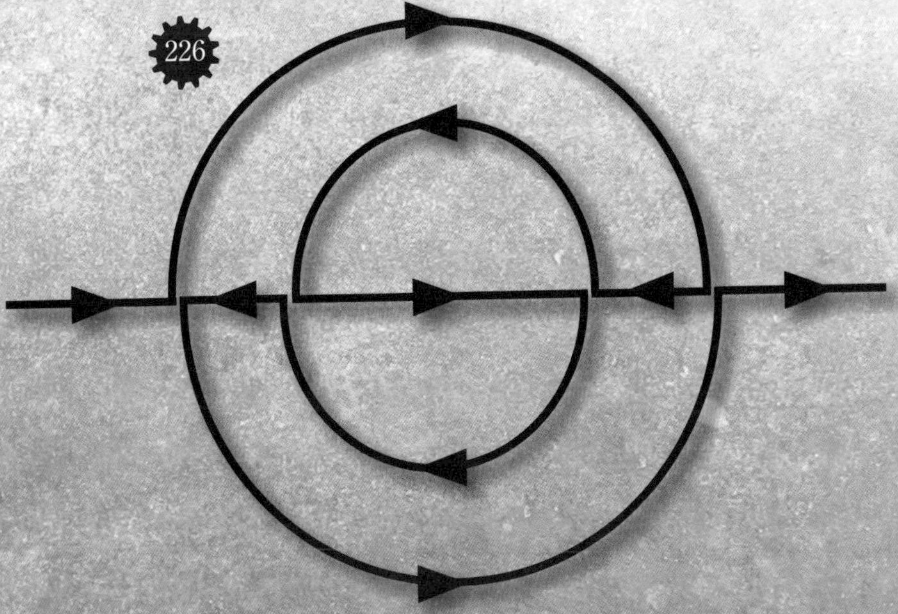

3 x 5694 = 17082

228

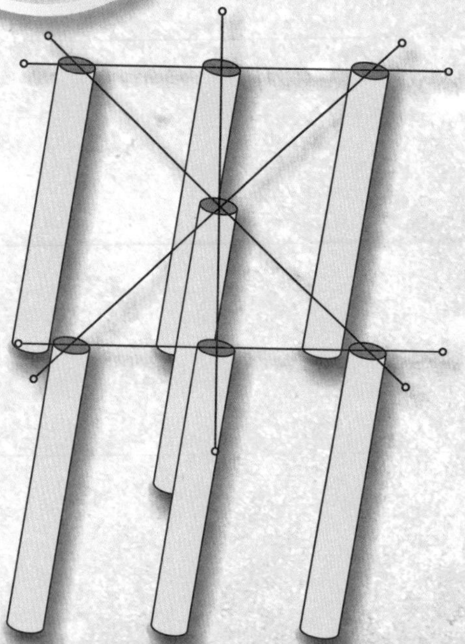

229 3800

230 She says: 'You will not give me the copper or silver coin.' If this is true, you get the gold coin. It cannot be a lie, because if it were a lie, it would have to come true!

231 Here's one way to do it: They order ABCDD on night 1, finding out what D is; AEFGG on night 2, finding out G and A, which they had also ordered on night 1; and BEHII on night 3, finding out what I, B and E are. This leaves C, F and H, which they ordered once each. C is the unknown dish from night 1, F from night 2 and H from night 3.

232 He replies, 'No, a sane person would pull the plug!'

They have five children.

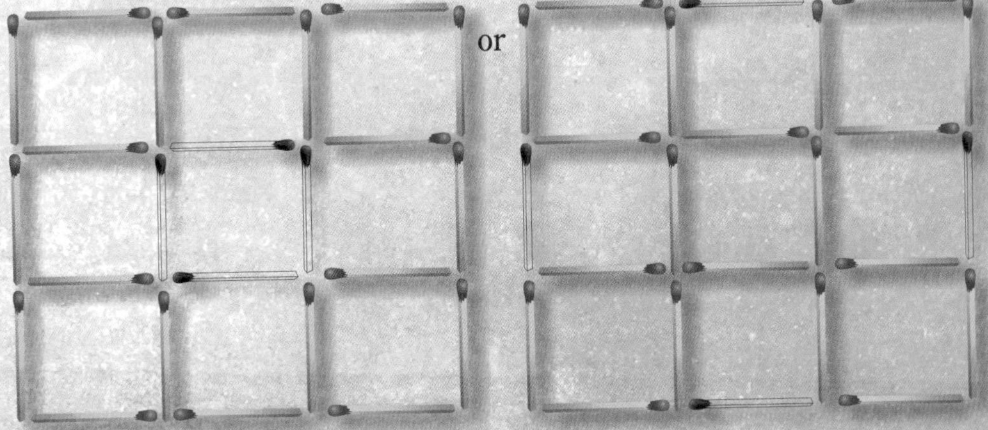

102 becomes 10^2, or 100, so
$101 - 10^2 = 1$

He divides the cards into piles of 42 and 10, then turns the whole pile of 10 over.

21 pounds.

Yes. He makes 10 pounds on each deal, so he is 20 pounds up at the end of the day.

He should choose to be thrown into the pit of lions. If the lions have not eaten for five months, they will be dead!

There will be 21 holes.

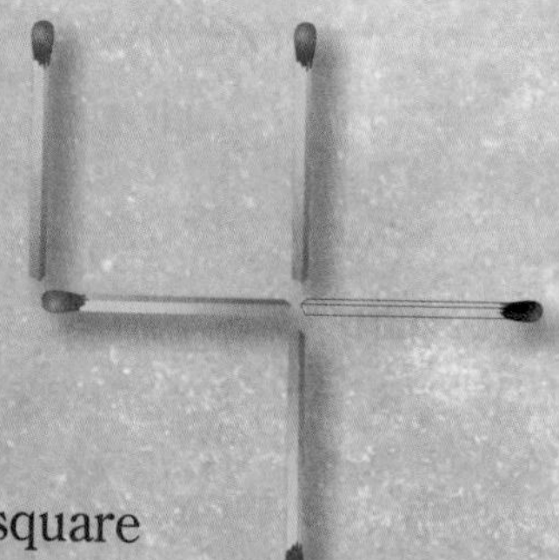

4 is a square number as it is 2 squared!

Emma won two games, and Jane won three games more than Emma, so they played a total of seven games.

246 They should open the gold box. If the will were in the silver box, all the inscriptions would be false. If it were in the lead box, all the inscriptions would be true.

177 – 77 = 100

He left the house at 7.05. The time he saw was 2.10 earlier than the real time. The mirror image is reflected across a symmetrical point of 6.00 (as this was morning). That means that the time he saw was 6.00 plus half of 2.10, which is 7.05. He thought the time was 4.55.

249 What we know:

	Before	Now
Mother	x	40
Son	y	z

$40 = 4y$, so $y = 10$

$z = x$

The difference in their ages is the same at all times, so:

$40 - x = x - 10$

This means that $x = 25$, so the son is 25 years old.

250 An hourglass.

251 After one team loses all its members, the team that it eliminates members from will always win. For example, if the red team is the first team to lose all its members, it is now impossible for the blue team to lose any members, so the blue team will eventually win. The best strategy is in fact to avoid answering questions until one team is eliminated, because any correct answer from one team will reduce the size of the second team that eliminates members from the third team. If all the players know this, none of them will ever answer correctly.

252

253 Just the three.

254 This is a scam, but not involving fixed races. The strang has been sending out thousands of emails every day, giving different predictions involving all the runners in the race, then sending out another prediction just to those who received the correct result in the previous race. At the start of the week, he sent perhaps 10,000 emails. Now he is left with a dozen or so potential suckers, and you're one of them!

255 The baby weighs 15 kg.
The cat weighs 6 kg and the woman weighs 81 kg.

256 2178 x 4 = 8712

257 She has two nephews and four nieces.
Beatrice has two daughters.
Carla has one son and two daughters.
Davina has one son.

258

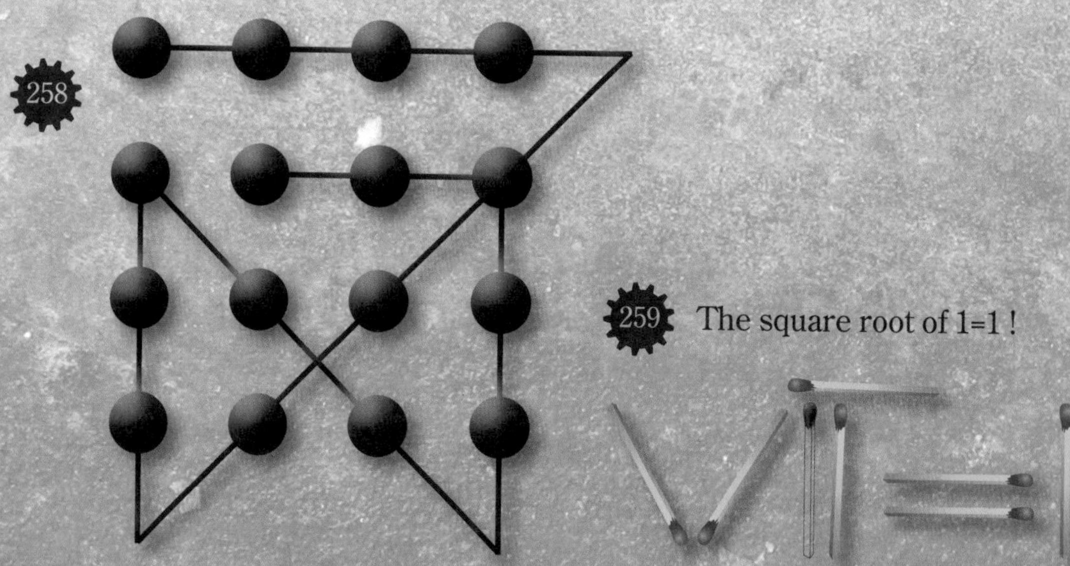

259 The square root of 1=1 !

260 The boy should carry 40/100 of the whole weight, so the pig should be hung 60/100 the length of the pole from the boy's shoulder. This means that it should be hung 90 cm from the boy's shoulder and 60 cm from the father's shoulder.

261 The spirit must be behind door D, meaning that just the inscription on door B is true.
If it were behind Door A, then B and D would be true.
If it were behind Door B, then A and D would be true.
If it were behind Door C, then A, C, and D would all true.

262 $5 \times (5 - (1 \div 5)) = 24$
$1 \div 5 = 0.2$
$5 - 0.2 = 4.8$
$4.8 \times 5 = 24$

263 The doctor is the boy's mother!

264

	6	4	
2	8	1	7
	5	3	

265 The bear must be standing at the North Pole, so presumably it is a polar bear and it is white.

266 6438. The digits shift along one place each time, moving to the front when they reach the end.

267

The late night film finished in the middle of the night. In 72 hours' time, it will also be the middle of the night, so it won't be bright or sunny.

The room Sylvester has walked into is a lift.

The calendar repeats itself every 28 years. The couple claim to have been married on that date 28 years ago, but the woman said they were married on a Sunday, and that date 28 years ago had to have been a Thursday.

81. Each term is the sum of the three preceding terms.

The three women share eight dishes, so they each consume $\frac{8}{3}$ dishes. Claire has only given away $\frac{1}{3}$ of a dish, while June has given away $2\frac{1}{3}$, which is seven times as much. So to be fair, Jennifer should pay June 7 pounds and Claire just 1 pound.

They were riding each other's horse.

276 It does not fall at all. His hands will meet in the middle of the pole!

-10. Each number is the previous number multiplied by -13.

Mother	Child	Age
Juliet	Jamie	3
Monica	Graeme	4
Laura	Dylan	2
Anne	Holly	1

Here is one way to do it.

The rest of the officers lost their head – Captain Blighty!

You need four colours. In fact, you only need four colours for any map, real or imagined.

Bruce has a moustache and stole the watch. Watson has a beard and stole the purse. Crusoe is clean-shaven and stole the wallet.

285 He folds each corner of the paper into the centre. This will give him a square that is exactly half the size of the original square, but double the thickness. He can do his painting on the opposite side of the paper to the folds.

286 To see how fair the game is, think of six gamblers each betting on a different number. Their total stake is £6. If three different numbers come up, three of the gamblers win £2, which cancels out the stake. If two numbers come up the same, one gambler wins £4 and another £2, again cancelling out the stake. If all three numbers are the same, just one gambler wins £6, which yet again cancels out the stake. So the game is entirely fair. In the long run, neither the house nor the gamblers win.

287

288

289 $1089 \times 9 = 9801$

290 None of the dots is actually there. If you focus on one intersection, the dot there disappears, but you can still see all the others.

291 He needs to be at least 25 cm away from the mirror. When you look at a mirror image, you see yourself as if the mirror image were the same distance behind the mirror as you are in front of it. So although James is only 25 cm from the mirror, the image of his face will look like it is 50 cm away, and it will be in focus.

292 There are now eight small diamonds and one large one.

293 The missing number is 6. The middle number of each set of three is the sum of the digits in the numbers either side of it.

294 It has moved 0.8 m. Before the slide, the top of the ladder was 2.4 m up the wall. This is worked out using Pythagoras' theorem: $2.4^2 = 2.5^2 - 0.7^2$. After the slide, the ladder is 2 m up the wall. Therefore, the square of the distance from the wall to the base of the ladder is now $2.5^2 - 2^2 = 1.5^2$. So the distance moved is $1.5 - 0.7 = 0.8$ m

295 It is 12 o'clock noon. It is also time to buy a new clock!

296

297 By the time Grace joins in, Helen has peeled 10 potatoes, so there are 45 left. Six minutes later, Grace has peeled 30 and Helen 12, leaving three left. Grace takes another 24 seconds to peel two more and six seconds later Helen finishes the last one. In total, from the time Helen started peeling, it took them 11 minutes 30 seconds to finish them. Helen peeled 23 potatoes, while Grace peeled 32.

298 The next year will be 2307. Increasing the second and third digits by 1 gives you the next 6 years after that: 2417, 2527, 2637, 2747, 2857, 2967

299 The cork is floating to the highest point in the water, which is at the edge of the glass, where the water clings to the sides. But if you fill the glass completely, the water will bulge in a convex shape above the sides, and the cork will settle at the centre.

300 The German owns the fish. Here is the full breakdown:

	Colour	Nationality	Beverage	Smoke	Pet
1	Yellow	Norwegian	Water	Dunhill	Cats
2	Blue	Danish	Tea	Blends	Horse
3	Red	British	Milk	Pall Mall	Birds
4	Green	German	Coffee	Prince	Fish
5	White	Swedish	Beer	Bluemast	Dogs